## Objectives

The aim of this unit is to introduce you to a way of thinking which has been found helpful in understanding and designing complex systems which involve many interactions between their parts. Many of the ideas are taken up again in later units of the course: indeed, the very idea of a system forms an important thread linking the individual units. It is therefore important that you should make yourself thoroughly familiar with the contents of this unit and look for examples of the concepts discussed in it in the world about you.

More specifically, when you have read the unit you should be able to:

(1) Explain in your own words what is meant by a system.

(2) Define the following terms as they are applied to systems: ecosystem, socio-technical system, component, link, state, variable, emergent property, transformation, single valued transformation, closed transformation, trajectory, discrete, continuous, deterministic, probabilistic, closed, open, input, output, control, open loop, feedback, lag, exponential lag, iteration.

(3) Decide whether a given system is open or closed, discrete or continuous, deterministic or probabilistic.

(4) Discuss different ways of classifying systems and the relationships between the classifications.

(5) Describe the principles involved in regulating a system and explain the instabilities which may arise as a result.

(6) Calculate the number of possible different states of a simple system.

(7) Express large numbers in the form $x \times 10^y$.

(8) State the two 'laws' of general systems, discuss the status of these laws and make simple deductions from them.

(9) Give examples of a number of systems and discuss where to draw the system boundaries.

(10) Describe the iterative mode of thinking which is often necessary in designing a system.

## What you have to do

There are short exercises, one each in sections 2, 6, 7 and 8, two in Section 9 and six in Section 5. We don't expect you to spend more than two or three minutes on any one of them.

The Appendix on the use of exponents for expressing large numbers contains 34 very short examples which might take you about fifteen minutes if you need to do them.

As soon as you have completed this unit you could, with advantage, start reading the Systems File.

1.20

The Open University

*The Man-made World: Technology Foundation Course Unit 1*

*The week number during which this unit should be studied is not necessarily the same as the unit number. Please consult your wall-chart study guide to the Technology Foundation Course to find the place of this unit in the course.*

# SYSTEMS

*Prepared by John Beishon*
*for the Technology Foundation Course Team*

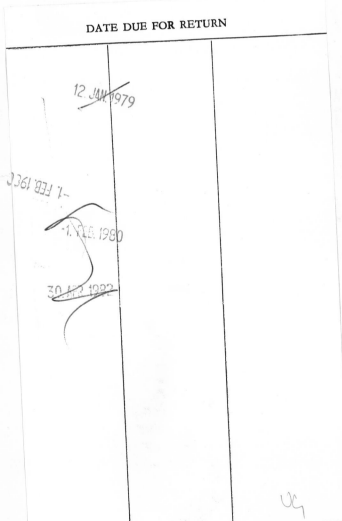

THE OPEN UNIVERSITY PRESS

## The Technology Foundation Course Team

| | |
|---|---|
| G. S. Holister | *(Chairman and General Editor)* |
| K. Attenborough | *(Engineering Mechanics)* |
| R. J. Beishon | *(Systems)* |
| D. A. Blackburn | *(Materials Science)* |
| J. K. Cannell | *(Engineering Mechanics)* |
| A. Clow | *(BBC)* |
| G. P. Copp | *(Assistant Editor)* |
| D. G. Crabbe | *(Course Assistant)* |
| C. L. Crickmay | *(Design)* |
| N. G. Cross | *(Design)* |
| E. S. L. Goldwyn | *(BBC)* |
| J. G. Hargrave | *(Electronics)* |
| R. D. Harrison | *(Educational Technology)* |
| M. J. L. Hussey | *(Engineering Mechanics)* |
| A. B. Jolly | *(BBC)* |
| J. C. Jones | *(Design)* |
| L. M. Jones | *(Systems)* |
| R. D. R. Kyd | *(Editor)* |
| J. McCloy | *(BBC)* |
| R. McCormick | *(Educational Technology)* |
| D. Nelson | *(BBC)* |
| C. W. A. Newey | *(Materials Science)* |
| S. Nicholson | *(Design)* |
| G. Peters | *(Systems)* |
| A. Porteous | *(Engineering Mechanics)* |
| C. Robinson | *(BBC)* |
| R. Roy | *(Design)* |
| J. J. Sparkes | *(Electronics)* |
| R. Thomas | *(Economics)* |
| G. H. Weaver | *(Materials Science)* |
| P. I. Zorkoczy | *(Electronics)* |
| and the late Professor R. K. Ham | *(Materials Science)* |

The Open University Press
Walton Hall, Milton Keynes

First published 1971. Reprinted 1974 (with corrections), 1975 (twice)

Printed in Great Britain by
Martin Cadbury, a specialized division of Santype International,
Worcester and London.

SBN 335 02500 5

Open University courses provide a method of study for independent learners through an integrated teaching system, including text material, radio and television programmes and short residential courses. This text is one of a series that makes up the correspondence element of the Technology Foundation Course.

The Open University's courses represent a new system of university-level education. Much of the teaching material is still in a developmental stage. Courses and course materials are, therefore, kept continually under revision. It is intended to issue regular up-dating notes as and when the need arises, and new editions will be brought out when necessary.

For general availability of supporting material referred to in this book, please write to the Director of Marketing, The Open University, P.O. Box 81, Milton Keynes, MK7 6AT.

Further information on Open University courses may be obtained from the Admissions Office, The Open University, P.O. Box 48, Milton Keynes, MK7 6AB.

# Contents

**Section 1**

# Introduction

This unit is about systems, about what they are and why we think it is useful for you to know about them. It is also about the *systems approach* which has become popular in recent years. Not long ago the term system was hardly used except in words like *systematic*, but the idea of a system has gradually assumed more and more importance which is reflected in the widespread use of the term. We are surrounded by and are a part of the *solar system*, we create and live in *political and social systems*, we dwell in *housing systems*, we grapple with *transport systems*, we suffer when our *internal systems* like the digestive system go wrong, and indeed the most important part of us is a vital and mysterious system, our *brain*, part of the *central nervous system*.

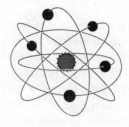

All these things are at first sight very different, so why are they all called systems? The reason is that they have one thing in common, they are all assemblies of different parts richly interconnected with each other. But the word system is nevertheless a problem word because although everyone knows (or thinks they know) what it means, it turns out to be surprisingly difficult to define precisely. Before we have a closer look at definitions of the word system I want to explore the use of the term a little more.

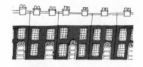

Systems are pervasive—they appear everywhere. They are found at both extremes of the size scale: the *solar system* is a vast assembly containing our sun and its planets, which in turn is only a minute part of our particular *galactic system* which is just one of countless such galactic systems spread through the observable universe. At the other extreme, biologists study *cell systems* and physicists *atomic systems*. There are *mechanical systems*, for example, engines and generators; there are *biological systems*, man and other animals, plants; there are *social systems*, factories, political parties, families. Where a mechanical and a biological system combine as when a man drives a car or pilots an aeroplane, we talk about *man–machine systems*. Then there are *natural systems* which can work away on their own without human intervention, for example, forest systems, weather systems, river systems.

Some of these natural systems which relate particularly to the environment of man and animals and form the basis of our food and support systems, are called *ecological systems*, or *ecosystems* for short. In recent years man has interfered more and more with these ecosystems to meet the growing needs for more food, water and commodities but unfortunately he has not appreciated the system nature of the situation or the extent of the systems. The results have sometimes been disastrous and totally unexpected; it is probable that, unless we do quickly understand the system nature of ecosystems and take some preventive action, we shall starve or pollute ourselves out of existence. Some people even think that it is too late to avert the consequences of pollution at all.

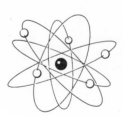

The Systems Dynamics Laboratory at the Massachusetts Institute of Technology has worked on the analysis of global systems using computer models to simulate systems.* The models include natural resources, population levels, industrial investment and production, pollution, and so on. The effect of different policies can be studied by setting different levels for these variables and then letting the computer calculate the various possible consequences into the future. The results are very disturbing, for they suggest that under many conditions nothing can be done to avert disaster.

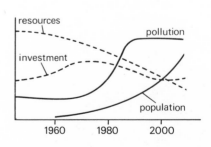

\* Forrester, J. (1971) *World dynamics*, Wright-Allen Press Inc.

This work has led to much controversy and many critics have attacked the 'doom' philosophy. Some people argue, for example, that advances in technology will change the situation dramatically. You will come across some more discussion about this controversy later in the course.

The latest developments in systems are probably to be seen in the growth of huge corporations and governmental organizations which are termed *socio-technical systems* because they combine technological systems with human management systems.

One thing to notice is that systems appear in a hierarchy, that is, in a structure where the large systems encompass the smaller systems, and the smaller systems themselves are made up of even smaller systems and so on. The gradual realization of the scope and range of systems has led to the development of a subject concerned with the concepts of systems in general and it is fittingly called *general systems theory*. This subject provides or attempts to provide an integrative framework for the analysis and understanding of systems—all kinds of systems.

general systems theory GST

Section 2

# Defining system

One way of discovering the meaning of a word is to look at all the different ways in which it is used by people and to try and isolate some common element or elements from these different uses. This common element is sometimes called the *core meaning*. An example of this process is given by Nehemiah Jordan* where he analyses the word *system*. I am not going to go through the steps in his analysis here but I will just give you the outcome. This is that the word's core meaning is made up of two aspects: an *out-there* aspect which refers to the actual system, and an *inside-us* aspect which comes from us, from the person doing the defining. Let us look more closely at these two aspects.

The out-there aspect of a system *is* the system. It seems to be clear from the way that the word is generally used that a system is a collection of parts or entities which are joined or connected together in some way. The solar system consists of the sun and our nine planets which are connected or linked to the sun and each other by gravitational forces. A *transport* system consists of track, trains, goods, stations and passengers, all connected together in various ways. A *cell* is a system, which consists of a membrane, protoplasm, a nucleus and so on, again all interlinked or connected together. In the universe there are almost an infinite number of systems of different kinds, all with separate parts connected together, but on the other hand we do not call *every* connected set of parts a system.

This brings us to the second part of the definition, the inside-us part. An essential part of defining a system is the selection of that particular set of things to be called a system by the person doing the defining. This is really the cause of much of the difficulty we have had in the past in coping with these kind of words: we have looked for a completely independent definition, one which exists outside the person making the definition, but in fact *we* have had a direct hand in creating the idea of a system in each case because *we* are applying the idea and *we* are choosing what to include and exclude in each case. Remember too that when we do this choosing, we have a purpose in mind so that our definition depends to some extent on what we want to use the concept for. When my first draft of this unit was being discussed, several of my colleagues objected to the solar system being included as a system on the grounds that it exists as it is and just goes through a predictable cycle of events. After some discussion it turned out that they felt that systems are only worth identifying as such if man can see some way to affect the system or to *control* it. This is a very reasonable viewpoint and perhaps an understandable one in technologists as opposed to scientists!

This ability to choose our system boundaries gives us much flexibility in using the concept; we can regard the *cell* as a system on its own, but at another time we can treat an assembly of cells which make up an *organ*, such as the heart, as a system. To other people this organ may itself only be a component part of a larger system, a complete *organism* such as a rabbit or man for example. To a sociologist, people as organisms are just component parts of still larger systems, *social systems* such as families or trade unions.

---

* Jordan, N. (1968) *Themes in speculative psychology*, Tavistock Publications. (This article is reprinted in the Systems File.)

This illustrates my earlier point about systems being hierarchical, but the identification of a system may cut through or across this hierarchy. A man as an organism is a system, a disease which uses man as a host is a system which involves perhaps rivers, other animals, and insects as well. The man is a member of a family system, he may also be part of a political system, an organizational system, an information system and so on.

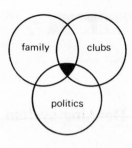

So far I have suggested that a system is a set of interconnected elements or parts which a person has identified as being worth isolating for consideration. There are, however, some immediate difficulties here. Suppose I take a box full of marbles. The marbles are parts, so is the box; if I take the box away the marbles will take up different positions so they are in a sense interconnected. The marbles near the bottom of the box carry the weight of those above them and they are slightly affected by this weight. But would you want to call this box-and-marbles a system? I should think most people would say 'no', although we could argue that the individual marbles *are* different in that the effect of taking away one at the bottom of the box is different to removing one from the top layer, so there is some degree of *organization* present. Perhaps a better example of this kind of arrangement is a dust cloud or a box full of gas molecules.

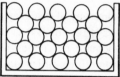

**Example 1**

Why do you think these examples are not really systems? Try to give two reasons.

For answer, see end of unit.

One way out of this difficulty is to say that these are in fact systems, but *unorganized* systems. They are characterized by the fact that the individual elements or parts are not connected together in any organized way—it does not make any difference which marbles are in which layer, for example. Also the relations between the parts are uniform and comparatively simple and it does not matter where each part is at any time. A better description of these things is probably *chaotic aggregates* and I would like to stick to this distinction between aggregates which have the properties described above, and systems. Systems are characterized by having parts which are connected in organized and complex ways, and another important point is that the parts of a system are likely to be changed if they enter or leave the system. Nothing happens to a gas particle if I either put it into the box or take it out again. A. Angyal* puts the distinction like this: 'In aggregates it is significant that the parts are added; in a system it is significant that the parts are arranged.'

chaotic aggregates

Another objection to my box-with-marbles or gas particles as a system is that it does not *do* anything. Systems surely should do things or at least be capable of doing things. Of course, this is partly a matter of the time-scale we are considering. The Himalayas mountain range does not *do* anything from our point of view, but over a very long time-scale they can probably be seen to be changing. They are eroded by the elements and altered by earthquakes, so on a geological time-scale they are changing. If you look at the tuning picture or test card on your TV set it does not appear to be changing, but in fact a new picture is being created once each 1/25 of a second. Our eyes and brain normally do not register things which change as fast as this.

This interest in behaviour is fundamental to the study of systems and, in fact, when you think about it, we are not so much interested in how the components of a system work as in the *behaviour of the total system*. I do not suppose that you know, or care very much, whether the car you

* Angyal, A. (1941) *Foundations for a science of personality*, Harvard University Press. The relevant part is reproduced in Emery, F. E. (ed.) (1969) *Systems thinking*, Penguin Books.

travel in has an alternator or a dynamo to charge the battery and to provide electric power. You are more concerned with whether the car starts or runs smoothly when you want to use it. When you use the telephone for a long-distance call the message may be transmitted in a number of different ways. It does not matter to you whether the signals go by radio, cable link, microwave or radio satellite, as long as they get there. This is not to say that the components of a system and the way that they work are never important, only that the total system behaviour is usually of more interest.

One other point about system behaviour: later in this unit we shall be dealing with the control of systems and it is worth noting that the 'behaviour' of a system may appear as 'non-behaviour' although the system may be very active indeed to produce this non-behaviour. For example, you are not normally concerned with your body temperature. It is usually controlled fairly closely at about 36°C and so long as it does not change much you are happy with it. To keep the body at this temperature is not easy because, of course, the outside temperature is always changing and you are sometimes very active, producing excess heat, and at other times remaining still and dependent on the heat generated within you. So what we observe is the unchanging aspect of system behaviour, a steady temperature, but this is achieved by the continuous activity of a complex heat control system within the body.

So we can summarize our definition of a system as:  *definition of a system*

(1) An assembly of parts or components connected together in an organized way.

(2) The particular assembly has been identified by a human being as of special interest.

(3) In general, the parts are affected by being in the system and they are changed if they leave it.

(4) Our assembly of parts does something (but remember that behaviour may be *not* doing something when the outside world changes).

It is worth adding here that in several places in this section and in other parts of the unit, tricky points of definition or meaning arise. These philosophical questions can be very interesting but to go into them would take us into the realm of philosophy and not systems. The important thing is that the general idea should come across even if there are points where the meaning is a little imprecise. I suppose a philosopher would say that this is very important and he would devote much of the available time and space to an examination of these points, but as I have said, this is *not* a unit on philosophy! One attempt to provide a set of systems concepts has been made by Russell Ackoff* and it is worth while having a quick look at his list, if only to see how difficult it is to be precise *and* clear.

* Ackoff, R. L. (1971) 'Towards a system of systems concepts', *Management science*, **3** (11). Reprinted in Beishon, R. J. and Peters, G. (eds.) (1972) *Systems behaviour*, Open University Press/Harper & Row.

# Studying systems

In recent years there has emerged a new kind of man, the *systems man*. He uses *systems thinking* and the *systems approach*. He has developed new disciplines with names such as *systems engineering* and *systems analysis*. What have all these got to do with systems and why have they emerged now? There are many reasons, of course, but two important ones are as follows:

Scientists and technologists have been very active over the last hundred years and they have nearly exhausted the relatively simple areas of study which are open to them. This is not to suggest that these activities have been easy, far from it, but to emphasize that scientists quite sensibly tackle simple and less complex things first before trying to understand more complex things.

A second reason is that there has been a slow but steady increase in the complexity of man-made systems and also in the extent to which we are able to interfere in the natural biological, geological and ecological systems of the Earth.

As a consequence of these two considerations, scientists and technologists have begun to turn their attention to the study of more complex systems and to try to develop tools to analyse their behaviour. A powerful motivation for this interest is the rapidly increasing need to gain more control over what is happening in, and to, human societies and the environment as a result of the application of technological advances. This need for control arises in commercial and industrial operations as well as in our concern with our health, welfare and comfort. Another point which we will come back to later is that it has become clear that no one specialist can tackle and solve these new problems; the need has emerged for cross-discipline or multi-discipline approaches.

Of course, as with most new approaches, the systems approach turns out not to be all that new or revolutionary, but to be a new name for what people have done in the past. It has emerged as a new thing, however, partly because some real advances have been made not just in understanding something about *a* system's behaviour, but also about system behaviour in a more fundamental and general sense. We now know something about the laws which underlie the behaviour of *all* systems. This has coincided (as I have said earlier) with our slow realization that the behaviour of complex systems must be understood if we are to exercise some control over our lives and to avoid the consequences of some of our less well thought out actions.

**Section 4**

# Some terminology

At this point it is probably a good idea to introduce a set of terms which we can use to talk about systems and system behaviour. A common language is always useful and once you get used to it you will find it economical because you will be able to follow the discussions and arguments more easily. Unfortunately, as with many other disciplines, new words or old words with new specialized meanings have been introduced into the systems field. I shall try to introduce just enough specialist terms to aid clarity without going too far into jargon.

## 4.1 System boundary

The range and variety of systems is so great that we need a very general description to cover the many different things we are going to be dealing with. The first point to make is that any system must have some limit to it. It cannot include everything in the universe unless we are dealing with the one special system, the universe as a whole. So there is always an outside to a system, which we call the *system's environment*, and an inside, the system itself. The two things are separated by a system boundary as shown in Fig. 1. Note that a component can be part of two different systems at the same time.

*system environment*

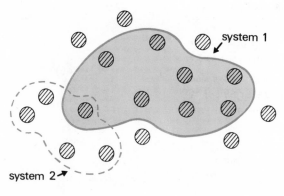

*Fig. 1*

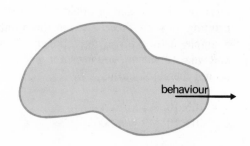

*Fig. 2*

As we have seen earlier, our interest is usually in the behaviour of the system so we can draw it as shown in Fig. 2.

In real life we find ourselves frequently dealing with systems where we have little, if any, idea about what is inside the system or how the internal parts work. Biological systems are good examples of these though we are gradually gaining more understanding of how they work. We refer to these systems as *black boxes*, because we know the system boundaries but we cannot see anything inside. (The box part probably comes from the fact that most people use boxes in diagrams to outline things. They look neater than my oddly shaped systems and they are easier to reproduce, or it may be that we are used to building complicated things in boxes, the insides of which are a mystery to most of us.*)

*black boxes*

---

\* The name could have come from the work of Harold S. Black who in 1923 was studying the properties of amplifier circuits and introduced 'boxes' into his circuit diagrams to represent bi-conjugate devices.

Many systems have to be treated as black boxes because we cannot at present find out what exactly goes on inside them but there are sometimes advantages in treating things as black boxes even when we do know, or could find out, what goes on inside. The biological cell is a system and we do know a good deal about its internal structure and functioning but when we want to consider the properties of an organ, say the heart, we can treat the individual cells as black boxes. This means that we are interested in them as complete entities and we only want to know what happens to them when we put certain inputs into them. That is, we are interested in the relationship between input conditions and the resulting outputs and not in *how* they are connected. There are many other examples: the famous animal-conditioning procedures of B. F. Skinner* treat an animal as a black box. In this case the animal is trained to do certain things, like press a lever, by the careful giving or withholding of a reward (technically a reinforcement). By this means the behaviour of the 'animal system' can be controlled. We do not necessarily know exactly how or why it happens but we can make use of the reproducibility of the connections or relations which we discover between inputs and outputs. Most primitive agriculture is done like this. We know that sowing seeds in certain ways at certain times produces plants we can use later on but we do not necessarily know what goes on between sowing and cropping. However, we shall be dealing in more detail with system behaviour later on.

Setting the boundaries of a system may seem to be an easy thing to do but often turns out to be rather difficult. The boundary to our solar system seems obvious enough because the distances within the system are so much smaller than the distance to the next object 'outside' the system. For example, the distance from the furthest planet, Pluto, to the sun is about 3 666 000 000 miles, so the diameter of Pluto's orbit around the sun is about twice this, say 7 500 000 000 miles. The nearest star, Proxima Centauri, is 25 000 000 000 000 miles away from our sun and this is so much further than the distance across our solar system that we can clearly 'see' the boundary.

Incidentally, we shall be using very large numbers, and some very small ones, in this unit and in other units in the course. To save the bother of printing out all those zeros in the numbers you have just read we use a simple method involving exponents. If you know what an *exponent* is and what $10^6$ means, you need not read any more of this paragraph. If you do not then look at this:

    exponent

$$10 \times 10 = 100, \text{ and}$$
$$10 \times 10 \times 10 = 1\ 000$$

A simple way of writing these numbers is to say that 100 is 10 multiplied by itself, so we can signify this by writing $10^2$. The 2 stands for two tens multiplied together. In the same way $10^3$ is three tens multiplied together to give 1 000. This little 2 or 3 written above the ten is called the *exponent*, and it can be any number we like. There are some exercises for you to do in Appendix 1 which will give you the idea but notice that we can write 200 as $2 \times 10^2$, and 3 700 as $3.7 \times 10^3$. So the distance of Proxima Centauri is more easily written as $25 \times 10^{12}$, that is, 25 multiplied by 10 multiplied by itself 12 times.

Now, to get back to the system boundary. If we look at a more difficult case you will see that the boundaries are not so obvious. Suppose we are concerned with a transport system, a local railway line for example. We might consider the economics of its operation and decide that a particular line can never be profitable and close it down. But the effects of such a

* Skinner, B. F. (1961) *Cumulative record*, Appleton-Century-Crofts Inc.

change can be widespread. Previously satisfactory bus services may become suddenly overcrowded and inadequate. The roads may become congested, more accidents may occur; more cars may be sold which increases the prosperity of local garages and motor salesmen. People's lives may be changed in quite unexpected ways. The lesson is that a transport system is not just a single railway line, it includes all the different ways in which people might travel and also the reasons *why* they are travelling. Our system boundaries are wider than we might think and knowing how and where to draw them is one of the skills which the systems man tries to acquire.

## 4.2 Components and links

I have defined a system as being an interconnected set of parts, or elements, or entities, which we have identified as being of particular interest to us. It is clumsy to keep using different terms for the parts and connections so from now on I am going to talk about *components* as the constituents of systems, and *links* as the connections.

components
links

## 4.3 System state

The concept of a *system state* is a useful one and we shall use it a good deal in this and other units. The components are usually things or objects and the properties attached to them. If our component was a billiard ball, it would have a particular mass, shape, size, colour, temperature, surface texture, reflectivity, etc. For any component there will be an almost infinite number of different properties which we could define, examine and measure. These different properties of something are often called *variables* because they are things which can vary. Most of these variables can vary only between certain limits or the thing will no longer be identifiable as that particular object. A billiard ball can be almost any colour or reflectivity but it cannot be much larger than, say, two inches in diameter, nor smaller than about one inch or it will no longer be in the class of things we call billiard balls. Each variable of our ball will have a particular value at any one moment and we could make an accurate description of our ball by setting out a large number of the different values for that ball. As you can see from this example some of the variables are virtually fixed, the shape of a billiard ball cannot vary much if it is to remain a billiard ball, but its position in space can and does.

variables

When we come to study the behaviour of individual systems we shall probably only be interested in the changes which occur in one or two of the variables of the components or of the system. With a billiard ball, we are usually interested in its motion, that is its velocity, which tells us how fast and in which direction it is moving. The colour, elasticity, reflectivity, and so on, will not change during the time we are concerned with the system (although over a long time-scale these things might change and we could then be very concerned with them), so we concentrate on the motion alone.

In this example the variable we are interested in is fairly obvious but in other cases it may not be so clear. However, it is the system state we are dealing with here and we can define this as the *set of values for the variables we are concerned with at that particular moment in time*. Although up to now I have talked about systems as being components linked together, you can see that it could make more sense to regard a system as the set of *variables* which we are dealing with. This raises a number of important points but we shall not be able to develop them further here.

system state

# System behaviour

The distinguishing feature of the systems man with his systems approach is that he is interested primarily in the *behaviour of the total system* which he has identified or defined. Why should the behaviour of systems attract so much interest and why should it apparently raise difficulties? I hope I have given enough illustrations to convince you that we have good reason to be interested in system behaviour but why is it difficult to analyse it? Perhaps the most surprising thing which has emerged from this 'new' systems approach is a realization of the unbelievable complexity of even simple systems. How can simple systems be complex? Let me use an example from Ross Ashby* to show you.

Imagine an array of ordinary light bulbs, say a display of $20 \times 20$ bulbs arranged in a square pattern so that there are 400 bulbs altogether. Let us regard this as our system. We can think of the behaviour† of this system as the many different ways the array of lights can light up. If each bulb can be either *on* or *off*, then the behaviour of our system at any moment is the pattern showing on the array. Each pattern is one of the system states for this system. The interesting question is: how many different patterns can this simple system display? If we start with all the lamps *off*, this would be one pattern, and with them all *on* this would be another. Between these two extremes we can have a large number of different arrangements of lights on and off. The surprising thing is just how many different patterns or states there can be.

**Example 2**

How many different patterns would you think this array of 400 lights could show? 400? 4 000? 40 000? 400 000? Many more than any of these?

For answer, see end of unit.

In this system there are just

$$2^{400}$$

different arrangements and this is roughly‡

$$10^{120}$$

This is a 1 followed by 120 zeros and it would be difficult to write it out on this page. It is clearly quite a large number, but how large is it?

---

* Mesarović, D. (ed.) (1964) *Views on general systems theory*, John Wiley.

† Normally I will use 'behaviour' to mean the way a system changes from state to state but in this instance I want to draw your attention to each state, a frozen piece of behaviour if you like.

‡ To convert $2^{400}$ to a power of 10 we use logs.
$$2^{400} = 10^x$$
$$400 \log 2 = x \log 10$$
$$\therefore x = \frac{400 \log 2}{\log 10} = \frac{400 \times 0.3010}{1} = 120.4 \quad \therefore 2^{400} \simeq 10^{120}$$

It has been estimated that in the whole universe as we know it, there are some $10^{73}$ atomic particles. So you can see that we would have an immediate problem if we tried to count up to $10^{120}$ using one particle for each count. This would be like counting on a child's counting frame or abacus where you push one bead along for every count you make. We would run out of atomic beads long before we reached anywhere near our $10^{120}$ patterns. In fact, $10^{120}$ is a very large number indeed. Even on a geological time-scale these numbers are still very large. The earth was in a gaseous state around $5 \times 10^9$ years ago, this is about $1.6 \times 10^{17}$ seconds and if we were able to work in the smallest unit of time that the fastest computers use, a nano-second ($10^{-9}$ seconds),* then we would have had something like $1.6 \times 10^{26}$ nano-seconds to work with since the earth solidified. So even if we had started counting our $10^{120}$ when the earth began, and made a count every nano-second (remember that is every $\dfrac{1}{1\,000\,000\,000}$ of a second) then we would still need a further length of time to complete our counting. In fact, we would need another $10^{104}$ years and, as you can see from the above, we have only had $5 \times 10^9$ years so far which means that we would have hardly got started on the task.

If you are slowly becoming convinced that our 400 lights are able to 'behave' in quite a large number of different ways, consider the newscaster in London's Leicester Square. A newscaster is one of those displays of lights where the words move along in a string one after the other, they are just like our array of 400 bulbs but longer. The one in Leicester Square has 30 000 bulbs in it and so it could display about:†

$$10^{9\,030} \text{ or nearly } 10^{104}$$

different patterns. This is a good deal larger than our previous $10^{120}$ yet it is actually a system in everyday use giving out messages to people and I do not expect that they think of it as unusual.

Numbers of this size are impossible to comprehend. The usual ways of illustrating size are quite useless here—these numbers are far, far larger than astronomical distances or times and it is hard to think of a way of conveying the implications of such numbers. However, if you think we have reached a large enough number think about this: we have somewhere around 10 000 000 000 nerve cells in our brains, that is: $10^{10}$. Suppose that each nerve cell could be in only one of two states like the lamps, either conducting a nerve impulse or not. (Nerve cells are in fact much more complex than this and can take up many more states than just two.) How many different states could our brain exist in? Well, it is quite a few, in fact it is

$$(2)^{10^{10}} \text{ or nearly } 10^{(3 \times 10^9)}$$

Perhaps you will be more impressed if I write it out like this:

$$10^{3\,000\,000\,000}$$

If we took as an absurd but interesting idea that a single 'thought' was one particular pattern of nerve cell conduction, then it is not surprising that we have such a fantastic range of thoughts or that some of them are so strange!

Ross Ashby‡ has summed up the problem neatly; he calculates that the maximum computing power available is about $10^{100}$. He says: 'The systems theorist may thus be defined as a man, with resources not possibly exceeding $10^{100}$, who faces problems and processes that go vastly beyond this size.'

---

* If you don't understand $10^{-9}$ turn to Appendix 1 at the end of this unit.

† $2^{30\,000} = 10^{9\,030}$, and $9\,030 \simeq 10\,000 = 10^4$

‡ Mesarović, D. *op. cit.*

Ashby's point is that the maximum computing power available to us is of the order of $10^{100}$ because we couldn't count to this number if we had made a count every nano-second since the earth solidified. But clearly the mental resources of the brain do go beyond these physical resources since the number of possible brain states is so large; the rate at which the states can change from one to another is very limited, of course, and this poses a problem, but nevertheless the brain is an immensely powerful tool. Whether its resources are sufficient to enable it to understand itself is an interesting and, at the moment, rather a philosophical point.

This then is one reason why it can be difficult to predict what even a simple system might do, there are such an enormous number of different states it could be in. I find it much more surprising and interesting that we can predict the behaviour of anything at all in the circumstances; we do after all make a fairly good job of predicting what that most complex of systems, another person, might do next. This is another important topic which we shall have to leave out for the moment, but the way we can reduce the problem of all these states to a manageable number clearly deserves attention. One thing you may have noticed in the above discussion is that the possible patterns, that is the different states which are possible, increase quite considerably as we add more components to the system. You can see that a very simple system with one component, which can exist in two states (say a single light bulb), increases its possible states to four when another bulb is added. This is shown in Fig. 3.

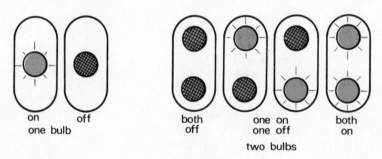

on      off

one bulb

both        one on        both
off         one off        on

two bulbs

*Fig. 3*

**Example 3**

Now have a go at working out how many states there can be with another component, making three in all, and then with four. Can you work out what the general rule is for a system with *n* components?

For answer, see end of unit.

It may have been this observation of the increase in the range of possible behaviours or states which even simple systems can display as more components are added which led people to think that there is something special about a system. Incidentally, I have been talking about behaviours and states as if they were the same thing but I shall want to separate these ideas soon and reserve the term *behaviour* for the movement of a system from one state to another.

The number of states a system can take up is called its *variety*. A two-bulb system has low variety compared with our $20 \times 20$ bulb array.

variety

Take our two-component system of the two light bulbs, let's call them B1 and B2; there are four possible states of the two-bulb system as we have just seen. Now consider the different ways in which this system might change if it went from one starting state to another. Let us call a change from one state to another a *transition*. Suppose we started with both bulbs *off*, then either one bulb could come on next, or both could light up. We can set out all the possible system changes like this:

. transition

18

| Starting condition | Next system state |
|---|---|
| B1 and B2 OFF ⟶ | B1 ON, B2 OFF |
| B1 and B2 OFF ⟶ | B1 OFF, B2 ON |
| B1 and B2 OFF ⟶ | B1 ON, B2 ON |
| B1 ON, B2 OFF ⟶ | B1 ON, B2 ON |
| B1 ON, B2 OFF ⟶ | B1 OFF, B2 OFF |
| B1 ON, B2 OFF ⟶ | B1 OFF, B2 ON |
| B1 ON, B2 ON ⟶ | B1 OFF, B2 ON |
| B1 ON, B2 ON ⟶ | B1 OFF, B2 OFF |
| B1 ON, B2 ON ⟶ | B1 ON, B2 OFF |
| B1 OFF, B2 ON ⟶ | B1 OFF, B2 OFF |
| B1 OFF, B2 ON ⟶ | B1 ON, B2 OFF |
| B1 OFF, B2 ON ⟶ | B1 ON, B2 ON |

This gives us twelve transitions from any one system state to another. As you can see, it is rather tedious to write out all the possibilities even for a simple system like this. I could have saved myself some trouble if I had attempted to calculate the answer. I could have reasoned that there were only four possible starting conditions, and since each of these had to be followed by another state, there could only be three possibilities for each of the four starting states. I have only three because I am not counting a change from one state to the *same* state as a change. So I have $4 \times 3$ changes, which is my 12.

**Example 4**

Now work out how many behaviours or changes there are if this simple system changes twice in succession, that is, if it goes from one starting state to the next state, and then on to another state. Don't forget that this third state can be the same as the starting state. You can write all the possible transitions down if you like or you can try to calculate them. You will probably find it easier if you label each different state like this:

| Both off | = A | B1 off, B2 on = C |
|---|---|---|
| B1 on, B2 off | = B | B1 and B2 on = D |

Now try the same thing for three successive changes or behaviours.

Can you find out the rule for any number of transitions?

For answer, see end of unit.

In the above sequences we allowed a state to appear more than once, for example, for two successive changes we could have A→B→A or C→D→C. If we had limited ourselves to sequences where once a state has appeared it could not appear again, we would have had fewer possible behaviours, for example, with the four states A, B, C, D we would only have had:

| A B C D | B A C D | C A B D | D A B C |
|---|---|---|---|
| A B D C | B A D C | C A D B | D A C B |
| A C B D | B C A D | C B A D | D B A C |
| A C D B | B C D A | C B D A | D B C A |
| A D B C | B D A C | C D A B | D C A B |
| A D C B | B D C A | C D B A | D C B A |

This gives us 24 different arrangements of these four states if they can follow each other in any order but without repeats of states. Now let's go back to our not-so-simple system of 400 light bulbs: not only can they take up a large number of different states, but the possible behaviour

19

sequences the system can go through (even without repeats) is much larger again. The figure is:

$$(2^{400})!$$

The ! is not an exclamation mark to show surprise: we have already met $2^{400}$ as the total number of different states of the system. The ! is a mathematical sign (called a factorial) which means: multiply the number by every integer below it until you get to 1. So 4! is simply $4 \times 3 \times 2 \times 1 = 24$. Similarly, 10! is $10 \times 9 \times 8 \times 7 \times 6 \times 5 \times 4 \times 3 \times 2 \times 1$, which actually works out to 3 628 800.

A pack of ordinary playing cards has 52 different cards in it and you could deal these out in a line on a table in 52! different sequences. This is $52 \times 51 \times 50 \times 49 \ldots 3 \times 2 \times 1$. Even this is a pretty big number, larger than $10^{67}$. Perhaps by now you are getting sophisticated about large numbers and you find $10^{67}$ only fair sized. (After all you can take it away from our $10^{120}$ and it would make little difference to the size of $10^{120}$.) But our 400 light bulbs can go through $(2^{400})!$ different behaviours without even using each state more than once! This is a very large number indeed and it shows how relatively simple systems can generate an enormously varied amount of behaviour. I am going to stop trying to impress you with these numbers and simply make the point that the possibilities for the behaviour of even a simple system are just fantastic, and for a complex system incredible!

It may well have been this huge variety of behaviours that systems can display which led to the idea I mentioned earlier that systems are 'special'. The idea is that there is more to a system than just the combined properties of the individual components. This belief is sometimes expressed by saying:

*the whole is greater than the sum of its parts.*

The implication is that there is something extra in a system, something which only appears when the components are linked together in a special way. You may come across this idea referred to as the *emergent* properties of a system. The suggestion is that new or different properties emerge when a set of components are joined together to form a system. If this idea was true of relatively simple systems containing mechanical or electrical components, then you can see how appealing the idea is when we come to apply it to biological systems. There are so many components in biological systems that surprising emergent properties such as 'living' or 'reproducing' or 'self-organizing', which are so characteristic of these systems, can be accepted fairly easily.

emergent properties

However, if you think about this for a moment you might begin to wonder just where this extra something comes from and of what it might consist. Do we need this concept at all? Ross Ashby* in his book *Introduction to cybernetics* deals with this point and he suggests that the idea that new properties emerge from a system arises to some extent from our ignorance of the basic properties of the components in the first place. The example he gives is worth looking at:

If we have a flask containing a mixture of oxygen and hydrogen gases we have a colourless gas mixture which obeys the laws of gases. Suppose we now make an electric spark in the flask. The result is a reaction and a small amount of water is formed. This water is a liquid and it is nothing like the gases at all. Ashby points out that if all we knew about oxygen and hydrogen was that they were gases, then this result would be very surprising and it certainly would have been difficult to predict. If we know something of the atomic structure of matter, however, then the combination of the two gases to form water will not be surprising at all.

* Ashby, R. (1956) *Introduction to cybernetics*, Chapman & Hall; also published in University Paperbacks, Methuen (1964).

A second example, also taken from Ashby's book, is that of a piece of rubber. A rubber band is very stretchable and we might expect it to be made up of many long thin stretchable molecules. But, in fact, the molecules of rubber are not themselves stretchable or elastic; nevertheless when they are combined into a rubber band, the whole band *is* stretchable. Clearly this new property of elasticity emerges from our system of rubber molecules, but where has it come from?

**Example 5**

What possible explanation can you think of for this effect?

For answer, see end of unit.

These two simple examples show that the apparently new properties of systems may be present in the components in a potential form and that when the components are allowed to interact in a certain way, then these new properties appear. Ashby* states the situation as a theorem:

*The whole made by joining parts is richer in ways of behaving than the system obtained by leaving the parts isolated.*

The reasoning behind this is that although unjoined parts can exist separately in just as many total states as the joined system, the unjoined parts cannot influence the changes from state to state of other parts whereas the joined ones can. Hence the behaviours of the joined system are richer than those of the unjoined assembly.

## 5.1 Describing system behaviour

When a system behaves, i.e. does something, it changes from state to state. If we had a system which could exist in four states, let's call them $x_1$, $x_2$, $x_3$ and $x_4$, our system could behave like this:

Starts in state $x_1$
then $x_1$ goes to $x_2$
and $x_2$ goes to $x_3$
and $x_3$ goes to $x_4$
and $x_4$ goes to $x_1$

We can write these changes like this:

$T_1$

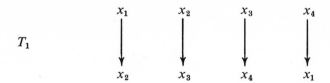

and this tells us that if our system exists in any one of the four states it will, it if changes, go to one, and only one of the other states possible. This specification of the changes which can occur is called a *transformation* and I have labelled the transformation set out above $T_1$. Notice that each state goes to only one other state and that there are no new states in the transformed system. If the first condition is met, going only to one state, the transformation is called *single-valued*. If the second is fulfilled (no new states), the transformation is called *closed*.

transformation

single-valued transformation

closed transformation

* Ashby, R. (1960) *Design for a brain*, Chapman & Hall.

Suppose that our system consists of three lights: a *red* one, a *green* one and an *amber* one. Let us call the state of the system when one red light is on $x_1$, with one green light $x_2$, with a red and amber together $x_3$, and with one amber alone $x_4$. You will recognize the system easily enough.

### Example 6

Can you now write down the transformation, call it $T_2$, for our standard British traffic light sequence?

| $T_2$ | $x_1$ | $x_2$ | $x_3$ | $x_4$ |
|---|---|---|---|---|
| | $x$ | $x$ | $x$ | $x$ ? |

For answer, see end of unit.

This pattern of changes from state to state which a system might go through is called its *trajectory*. Notice that I have not said anything about how quickly the system changes or why it changes, but only that *if* it changes it will do so in that particular manner. So a single change from one state to another is a *transition*, the specification of the possible changes, or the rule governing the changes, is a *transformation* and the actual pattern of changes from state to state is a *trajectory*.

trajectory

### Example 7

Can you now write down the trajectory for the pedestrian-operated light signal system (called the *x* way or Pelican crossing) as seen by the motorist? You may have to look it up in the Highway Code. Call it $T_3$ for the transformation and write the trajectory as series of states joined by arrows.

For answer, see end of unit.

The method of writing a transformation as shown above, and then a trajectory, can be tedious in many cases and there is always the problem of what to do with a system which does not have clearly defined separate states. Our billiard ball can be anywhere on the billiard table and as it rolls along it is difficult to say that it goes from state to state when it appears to move continuously. We shall come back to this point a little later on but we do need an easier method of writing down transformations. A useful method is as follows:

Take a variable of interest, call it $x$, then a new value of $x$ can be written as $x'$ which is the result of whatever happened to $x$. So if in our system we notice after a given time interval that the variable has doubled, then the transformation is written as:

$$x' = 2x$$

This might be the kind of transformation we would observe in a culture of bacteria where $x$ is the number at any one time and $x'$ is the number after one hour. We can express any number of changes in different variables of a system in this way; for example, if our system has three variables, $x, y$, and $z$, and they all change simultaneously, then a transformation $T_4$ could be:

$$T_4 \quad \begin{aligned} x' &= \tfrac{1}{2}x \\ y' &= 2y \\ z' &= x+y \end{aligned}$$

In each case the new values for $x$, $y$ and $z$ are obtained from the previous values.

**Example 8**

If the system started with initial values of

$$x = 100$$
$$y = 2$$
$$z = 0$$

then the transformation $T_4$ applied once would give what values for $x$, $y$ and $z$?

There is nothing to stop us applying $T_4$ again, and if we do this it is often written as $T_4^2$ to show that we have applied $T_4$ twice in succession. What are the values of the variables after $T_4^2$? And after $T_4^3$?

---

For answer, see end of unit.

---

This is a perfectly general method of describing system behaviour and it does have certain advantages over the apparently more complicated mathematical techniques which are usually used.*

---

* Ashby, R. (1956) *Introduction to cybernetics*, Chapman & Hall; also published in University Paperbacks, Methuen (1964).

# Different kinds of systems

Systems, as you will have gathered by now, come in all shapes and sizes. Some have very limited behaviours, like the traffic lights, and they have to go through the same trajectory over and over again once they have been activated. Other systems are extremely complicated and no one knows what they might do next or even how to find out. When scientists start to study something they usually begin by trying to classify the things they are looking at into a rational set of categories. The early biologists spent a great deal of time classifying and sorting the vast numbers of different animals and plants. We now have a comprehensive classification of these things which is based on certain fundamental principles. All animals with backbones are classed as Vertebrata, and they have certain things in common with each other which the Invertebrata do not have.

For some time people have been trying to find meaningful classifications for systems but it has proved to be a difficult process. Before we take a closer look at some of these attempts I want to talk about some of the different kinds of systems which will have to be fitted into classifications.

## 6.1 Discrete and continuous systems

We have already come across systems which exist in quite separate states like the traffic lights. These systems are called *discrete* systems. A discrete system is one which can exist in one, and only one, of a certain number of clearly defined and separate states at a time. The system cannot gradually fade from one state to another, it must jump in one go from state A to state B as when a traffic light signal changes from green to amber.

*discrete system*

Other systems, however, do not seem to have any clearly defined states and they move from one system state to another imperceptibly. Any moving system will normally change in this continuous manner; a car moving down a road will not jump from position to position, but will change its position continuously. We call this a *continuous system*. We might display the movement of a car down a road on a graph as shown in Fig. 4.

*continuous system*

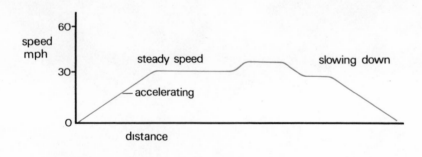

*Fig. 4*

Fig. 4 shows that the car started off, accelerated to 30 mph and then travelled steadily at this speed for some distance before going through a small speed change, perhaps to overtake another car. It then slowed down and eventually came to a stop. We could get the same kind of graph if we sat in the moving car and noted down the reading on the speedometer once every ten seconds. The graph would then be as shown in Fig. 5.

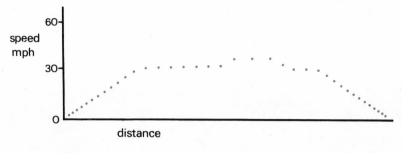

*Fig. 5*

Obviously this is almost the same graph as Fig. 4 except that we have a series of points instead of a single line. If we wanted a still more detailed picture of the movements of the car we would make more frequent observations of the car's speed, say once every second. And we could go on reducing the interval between each measurement or recording of the speed to achieve as much detail or accuracy as we want. The shorter the interval between each measurement the nearer we get to a continuous recording of the speed changes. In fact, it turns out that even though, in practice, we may be limited by the extent to which we can make extremely fast separate measurements, in theory we can always reach the continuous condition or as near to it as makes no difference. This may seem a little odd at first but the idea underlies some of the mathematics which you will meet later in our course and it will become clearer to you then.

So although we may wish to make a distinction between discrete state systems and continuous ones for certain practical purposes, we can always convert a continuous trajectory into a series of discrete values if we want to. And the conversion can be as accurate as we like by simply making the recording of the discrete values very frequent indeed.

## 6.2 Deterministic and probabilistic systems

What decides the trajectory of a system? In some systems, the sequence of states is completely decided beforehand and if the system changes its state then it *must* go to the next one in the sequence. Most individual traffic lights are like this. The trajectory of many American traffic lights is shown in Fig. 6 and the timing of the cycle is usually fixed; it is not affected by the cars coming along the road.

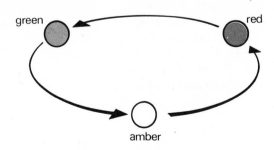

*Fig. 6*

Systems of this kind are called *deterministic* because the sequence of system states is predetermined.

deterministic system

Now consider a set of traffic lights controlling a road junction. Our system is now the *set of lights*. What about the trajectory of this set? In the most common case of a simple crossroads the sequence is determined: first green one way, then green the other. But look at the junction shown in Fig. 7.

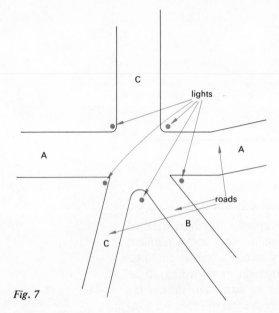

*Fig. 7*

The trajectory of the set of traffic lights (not of a single light) can be different depending on the arrival of cars along the different roads. If a car comes along road B, then the lights will soon change to green for that road, but after that they may go green on either A or C depending on whether any traffic came on either of those roads.

Another example of a system where the trajectory can vary is the roulette wheel. If you spin the wheel repeatedly, the output is a series of numbers and no one can say which number will come up next (unless the wheel has been fixed!). We might be tempted to say that the output of this system was completely unpredictable but, just as with throwing a pair of dice, we *can* say something about how often the different numbers will appear. The same thing applies to tossing a coin because over a large number of tosses we know that the ratio of heads to tails will be about 50/50 although we can never say which of the two is going to appear next on any one toss. Systems like this are called *probabilistic systems*. It is worth while making a distinction between those systems which are inherently probabilistic, such as the roulette wheel, and those like the traffic lights which depend to some extent on an outside event to determine or influence which state occurs next.

probabilistic systems

The distinction between probabilistic and deterministic systems (and in many ways between discrete and continuous ones) raises some of the philosophical issues I mentioned earlier. Discussion of these would take us beyond the scope of this unit. The important point to note is that although these systems may be different in some fundamental ways from each other, for practical purposes we can often *treat* them in the same way using suitable mathematical tools. The treatment of continuous systems by splitting the movement into very small discrete steps which I outlined in the previous section is one example.

## 6.3  Open and closed systems

One of the most important advances in systems science was made by L. von Bertalanffy* in the 1940s. He introduced the idea of an *open system* as opposed to *closed* systems. A *closed system* is, as its name implies, one

closed system

* Bertalanffy, L. von (1950) 'The theory of open systems in physics and biology', *Science*, **3**, 13 January 1950, pp. 23–9.

which does not take in or give out anything to its environment, whereas an open system can take in materials, energy or information and give them out again. Von Bertalanffy says:

> A System is closed if no material enters or leaves it; it is open if there is import and export and, therefore, change of the components. Living systems are open systems, maintaining themselves in exchange of materials with environment, and in continuous building up and breaking down of their components.

In a closed system behaviour results from interactions *among* the components of the system. Most of the familiar physical and chemical systems we come across in technology and science are effectively closed systems and their behaviour, in the theoretical sense, is governed by the laws of classical thermodynamics. In practice of course no real system is truly closed because we can never completely isolate a system from all outside influences, but nevertheless we can create situations where outside effects are negligible and can be disregarded. Closed systems are characterized by their inevitable movement towards a state of increased *entropy*. Entropy is a measure of the state of disorder in a system and the second law of thermodynamics which introduces this concept is elaborated upon later in the course.

So closed systems move towards an *equilibrium* state where the system comes to rest or reaches a state of internal balance. Another important characteristic of closed systems is that the final state they reach is determined by the initial or starting conditions. This means that, given a particular starting state, a closed system will always follow the same path to the final state.

*Open systems*, in contrast, display much more interesting open system behaviours. Von Bertalanffy describes them like this:

open system

> Even simple open systems show remarkable characteristics. Under certain conditions, open systems approach a time-independent state, the so-called steady state. The steady state is maintained in distance from true equilibrium and therefore is capable of doing work; as it is the case in living systems, in contrast to systems in equilibrium. The system remains constant in its composition, in spite of continuous irreversible processes, import and export, building-up and breaking-down, taking place. The steady state shows remarkable regulatory characteristics which become evident particularly in its equifinality. If a steady state is reached in an open system, it is independent of the initial conditions, and determined only by the system parameters, i.e. rates of reaction and transport. This is called *equifinality* as found in many organismic processes, e.g. in growth. In contrast to closed physico-chemical systems, the same final state can therefore be reached equifinally from different initial conditions and after disturbances of the process.

equifinality

The theory of open systems has been developed in several fields, notably by social scientists interested in applying systems ideas to social and psychological situations. The treatment of biological organisms and social organizations as open systems has proved fruitful and thrown new light on how these systems can behave.

## 6.4 Classifying systems

The last three sections have distinguished between systems in respect of certain specific attributes of the system: discrete *v.* continuous, open *v.* closed. These distinctions are useful for certain practical purposes such as selecting a technique for analysis, but there are other advantages in establishing classifications or *taxonomies* as they are called. For theoretical purposes it is important to be able to define the class of things to which a subject or approach applies and to distinguish among the sub-sets of things on theoretical grounds. But perhaps the most immediate value of a

taxonomy

taxonomy is in providing a mental framework or structure which helps us to grasp the range of the subject matter and the relations among its different aspects.

One example of this is the classification of systems into 'hard' and 'soft'. These represent two ends of a continuum and draw attention to relative amounts of knowledge about a system and about its aims or purposes. Hard systems are more easy to define and have clear-cut and often only a single aim or purpose. They are typically the subject matter of the engineer concerned with real-world constructions: mechanisms, machines, aircraft and chemical plants are all examples. This is not incidentally to say that these are necessarily easy to deal with, to design and operate; they can be very complex indeed. At the other extreme there are 'soft' systems, which are characterized by having human beings as components, are difficult to define, and do not have clear-cut and agreed aims or purposes. There is rarely any agreement about *the* aim of an organization, for example, and soft systems frequently have many different and conflicting aims which can even change over a period of time. In other words, the softer systems can actually set their own aims and change them.

Let us now look at two classifications which attempt to include a very wide range of different systems in some rational scheme.

The first is due to P. B. Checkland,* who has constructed a 'systems map' of the universe. The major divisions as he sees them are:

Checkland's systems map

(1) natural systems;
(2) designed physical systems;
(3) designed abstract systems;
(4) human activity systems.

His 'systems map', shown in Fig. 8, relates these systems to each other to build up a (or rather, the) universe.

The second example is a famous taxonomy due to **Kenneth Boulding.**† He sees systems as existing at a series of 'levels' like this.

Boulding's classification

(1) The first level is that of static structure. It might be called the level of frameworks: for example, the anatomy of the universe.
(2) The next level is that of the simple dynamic system with predetermined necessary motions. This might be called the level of clockworks.
(3) The control mechanism or cybernetic system, which might be nicknamed the level of the thermostat. The system is self-regulating in maintaining equilibrium.
(4) The fourth level is that of the 'open system', or self-maintaining structure. This is the level at which life begins to differentiate from not-life: it might be called the level of the cell.
(5) The next level might be called the genetic-societal level; it is typified by the plant, and it dominates the empirical world of the botanist.
(6) The animal system level is characterized by increased mobility, teleological behaviour and self-awareness.
(7) The next level is the human level, that is, the individual human being considered as a system with self-awareness and the ability to utilize language and symbolism.
(8) The social system or systems of human organization constitute the next level, with the consideration of the content and meaning of messages, the nature and dimensions of value systems, the transcription of images into historical record, the subtle symbolizations of art, music and poetry, and the complex gamut of human emotion.
(9) Transcendental systems complete the classification of levels. These are the ultimates and absolutes and the inescapable unknowables, and they also exhibit systematic structure and relationship.

* Checkland, P. B. (1971) 'A systems map of the universe', *Journal of systems engineering*, **2**, (2). Reprinted in Beishon, R. J. and Peters, G. (eds.) (1972) *Systems behaviour*, Open University Press/Harper and Row.

† Boulding, K. (1956) 'General systems theory: the skeleton of science', *Management science*, **2** (3) April 1956, pp. 197–208.

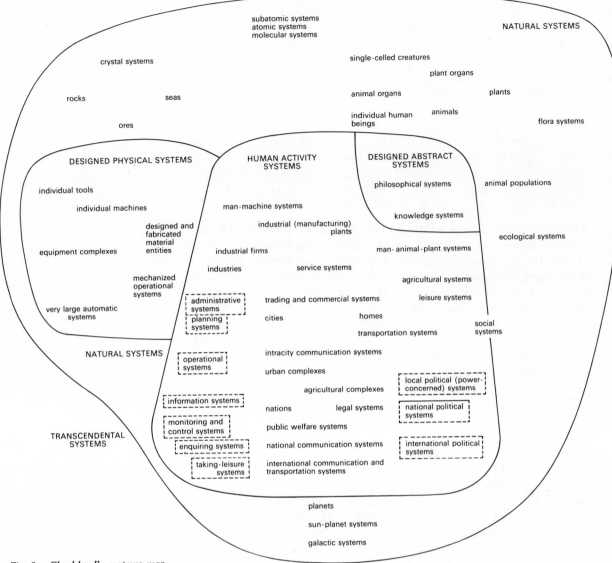

*Fig. 8   Checkland's systems map.*

Boulding's levels are related in a hierarchial structure, the higher-level systems being composed of lower-level ones and being generally more complex than those lower down.

The value of these taxonomies will increase when systems men have identified techniques or methods for analysing the different types of system and explored further their characteristics. If we then come across a new system, we could, hopefully, place it in the appropriate class or cell of our taxonomy and then readily identify important characteristics (which we might not have been aware of) and, perhaps more usefully still, identify the best or most appropriate analytical techniques to use. In practice we already do this so often that it has become a sub-conscious process greatly aiding us in dealing with real-world things. If you come across what appears to be a stone on the beach, say, our behaviour towards it changes markedly if we observe that it can move by itself. The reclassification from an *inanimate* to an *animate* system can be of enormous value. It could, for example, place the object in a 'food' system or 'danger' system.

# Pervasiveness of systems

So far my examples of systems have been largely the down-to-earth ones which we meet in everyday life but you can see from the two classifications mentioned above that other people include such things as language and symbol systems in their schemes. This is a reflection of the impact of this systems thinking which I have referred to from time to time.

The development of systems thinking has not been due to the introduction of these new system concepts, or to any special advances in control systems theory or engineering systems. There is a possible exception here in the growth of computer-based systems which in many ways go to the heart of the matter since computers are general-purpose machines which can, in theory, do anything in the way of information processing. But we shall be dealing with computers in several later units in this course so this point will be taken up again. In my view, the impact of systems thinking has arisen from the growing realization that the specialist sciences and fields of study, from physics to sociology, cannot on their own provide answers to many of the problems which man is now being forced to tackle. The older analytical approaches of the nineteenth century have been joined by the synthesizing approaches of the twentieth. We have begun to see that real systems do not fall conveniently into the traditional departmental divisions of science: one good example of this is the growth of the field of *man–machine systems* which has emerged from a combination of physiology, psychology and engineering. A man on his own is the proper subject matter for a physiologist or psychologist, a car is an engineering system, but the combined system, *man driving car*, crosses the boundaries. The results of this interdisciplinary approach can be seen in the improvements of car controls over the years. Uniformity of coding for the functions of knobs or switches enables us to cope with an unfamiliar make of car quickly; the size, shape and placing of the controls is now much more suitable for the driver, and the whole man–car system is designed with the interactions between the two in mind.

man–machine systems

### Example 9

Can you think of any other examples of new fields of study which cut across the older discipline boundaries?

For answer, see end of unit.

In the introduction to this unit I mentioned that there had emerged a specialist field of study concerned with the properties of systems in general, *general systems theory*. People interested in this area have largely been drawn from those traditional fields where the existing discipline was coming up against its limitations in its attempts to deal with more complex phenomena.

One of the first activities of investigators of a new field is collecting *data* and generally trying to establish the range of phenomena they have to deal with. The next step is to generate hypotheses and, where possible, to devise experiments to test them. The aim is to arrive at some kind of true statement about the relations among the phenomena. Such a statement is usually called a *law* or *principle*. Systems theorists have started this process of trying to find laws and two attempts are described in the next section.

**Section 8**

# Two systems 'laws'

One of the first things which must have been realized by even very primitive man was that there are regularities or predictable aspects to system behaviour. The sun rises and sets each day, the seasons change in a regular cycle, stones fall downwards and not upwards, and so on. The straightforward recognition of these regular patterns is of value in itself: man did not need to know why the seasons repeated themselves to take advantage of the fact and to develop agricultural methods. The early stages of any science consist in the production of descriptive laws about the behaviour of simple isolated systems (e.g. 'what goes up must come down'). This descriptive step is an important first stage in the scientific analysis of phenomena, but in many ways the next step is more important. This involves the formulation of a *quantitative* connection among the variables of the system.

Isaac Newton did not discover gravity—its existence was fairly obvious, nor was the idea that masses attract each other the most important feature of Newton's contribution. What Newton did was to formulate mathematically the laws concerning this attraction between masses. So scientists search for laws to describe the behaviour of systems. There are hundreds of laws which have been discovered and which are used to predict the behaviour of individual systems, but there is little in the way of laws about system behaviour in general. Here are two descriptive 'laws' which are the first steps in this process of making a scientific analysis of the phenomena of systems and of identifying system laws.

## 8.1 Requisite variety

You have already come across the idea that systems display variety, that is that they can exist in a very large number of different states. The 'law' of requisite variety simply states that if you are to cope with the behaviour of a system, you must have at least as much variety available to you as is in the system. Put this way it probably seems obvious but it is helpful to use an example to see how this works. This example comes from Ross Ashby,* the first man to draw attention to requisite variety.

'law' of requisite variety

A certain insect has an optic nerve which has 100 channels in it. Each channel can signal 20 yes/no signals along it per second. The insect may be faced by any one of ten different dangers, each of which can appear independently a second at a time. Can the insect's brain at the end of the optic nerve receive enough information to recognize or detect all the ten separate dangers so that it could take action to try to survive?

The answer is 'yes' because the *variety* in the dangers is 10 per second whereas the optic channel can transmit up to 2 000 signals per second. So the variety in the detector circuit is greater than the variety in the threat situations.

---

\* Ashby, R. *Introduction to cybernetics, op. cit.*

**Example 10**

Here is another example which you should be able to do. If the Ministry of Transport wanted to signal eight different messages to motorists, could the existing red, amber, green traffic light system do it? In other words, is the variety in the messages smaller than, equal to, or larger than the variety in the traffic signal system? Incidentally, how much variety is used in the present signalling system and does the system get fully used?

For answer, see end of unit.

## 8.2  Principle of equifinality

This arises from the distinction which L. von Bertalanffy* made between open and closed systems. It states that in a closed system the final state, that is the *equilibrium* state, can only be reached by one path and from a given set of initial conditions the system must follow one trajectory to the end state. An open system on the other hand can arrive at an end state by a number of different routes and from different starting conditions. This is a very fundamental property of open systems and one which makes open biological systems so very interesting. Scientifically, an open system is rather curious because it can be started off with one set of values and be left to run to a final state, and then re-started from a different set of initial values and still end up at the same state. This kind of behaviour is illustrated when a child is growing up and it suffers from some temporary illness which slows its growth rate down. After the illness is over, the child grows faster than the normal rate and tends to catch up to where it would have been if there had been no illness. A child's final height can be reached by different routes.

The idea of equifinality has had an impact on theories of social systems because it suggests that there is not one best and only way to run an organization to achieve a certain set of goals, but that many different routes can be taken to arrive at the same end state. Further discussion of these ideas is available in Bertalanffy's book.

* Bertalanffy, L. von (1968) *General system theory*, G. Braziller.

**Section 9**

# Control of systems

This section of the unit deals with the control of system behaviour. Our interest in control arises because we want to be able to bring about certain future states of the systems we are involved with, and it is this ability to produce a desired state at will which is the essence of control. It is important to make it clear at the outset that only a man can decide that he wants a certain future state to be brought about, only a man can set *goals*. This is not the place to develop arguments about whether machines can exercise control over other machines or over themselves, but I want to reserve the idea of a goal for use in relation to something peculiarly human or at any rate animal. Some systems or mechanisms do appear to 'control' themselves but I prefer to call this *self-regulation* rather than control although engineers tend to use the word regulation in a more specialized sense as you will see in the unit on Control.

goals

Let us leave on one side the problems associated with choosing goals and just concentrate on the exercise of control itself. Assume then that we have a goal state specified; to achieve it we must have a system that has this particular state in its repertoire of states and we must also have some means of influencing the trajectory the system moves along. So the three essentials for control are:

(1)   A goal state.
(2)   A system capable of reaching the goal state.
(3)   Some means of influencing the system's behaviour.

To achieve control, we then have to know something about the connections between the means of influence and the system's behaviour. If we don't know about this we must learn about it. Without this knowledge we are at the mercy of the system. Obviously we do not have the possibility of control if all we can do is watch and record or measure what a system does. This is not to say, however, that we cannot make use of such a system; I have already mentioned our use of seasonal cycles to grow foods: we cannot alter the seasonal changes but we can *take advantage* of them. So where we have uncontrollable systems that are nevertheless predictable, we can often make use of them.

In many simple systems the connections between the means of influence and the changes in the system are fairly easy to see or determine. It would not take us long to find out that turning a steering wheel clockwise turns a car to the right or that pushing a light switch down puts a light on. Unfortunately, we usually call these *means of influencing a system* the controls, and this can lead to some confusion when we talk about controlling a system. The steering wheel of a car is a *control* which we use to exercise *control*. Since when we influence a system via the 'controls' we are nearly always putting something into it we can refer to controls as *control inputs*, which avoids some of the confusion. So from here on I shall use *control inputs* for 'controls' like throttles, valves, steering wheels, etc. Notice that some of these enable us to exercise control over an actual input to the system, for example the throttle controls air and petrol inputs to a car engine.

control inputs

If we want to control a system, then we can operate on its control inputs and, provided that we know the connection between the control input settings or values and the system's behaviour, we can exercise the desired control. To avoid writing 'systems behaviour' all the time I am going to call this the *output* of the system. We can control quite complicated systems in this way and we usually do it by setting out a list of rules to be followed by rote. If I want to start my central heating system the *control rules* go something like this:

system output

control rules

(1) Turn main gas tap A on.
(2) Turn gas control valve B to red mark.
(3) Switch electrical supply on.
(4) Turn gas control valve B to 'pilot' position.
(5) Press down ignition lever C, hold it down until the gas lights and for a further 20 seconds.
  And so on.

This type of control is often called *open loop* for reasons which will become clear later. Remember it is essential to have knowledge about the relations between operations on the control inputs and the resulting effects on the outputs. Open loop control is only of limited usefulness because it depends for its success on the actual inputs to the system remaining fairly constant or *invariant* and on the relationship between control input setting and output value. In the real world, unfortunately for control purposes, things rarely stay unchanged for any length of time. For example, mechanisms wear and even metals can age or grow brittle over long periods of time. Open loop control can, however, work well in some circumstances; a good example of this is in my typing of the original of this sentence. I know the connections between the keys on the typewriter and the letters which appear on the paper. I know that these connections will stay the same and, of course, they are almost certainly the same on most of the other typewriters I am likely to come across. So I can get a desired system output, such as the phrase 'yours sincerely', by striking the keys y o u r s space s i n c e r e l y in turn. Touch-typists control their typewriters by open loop methods.

open loop control

**Example 11**

Can you think of any other everyday tasks which are open loop controlled? Write down three.

For answer, see end of unit.

What can I do if the connections, or some inputs to the system change from time to time in an unpredictable manner? This is a situation which always seems to happen to me in my shower. My goal state for this system is water gently falling on me at a comfortable temperature and it should be possible for me to set the hot and cold taps to the same setting each time to be sure of getting my comfortable temperature. But the inputs to this system include the temperatures of the hot and cold water supplies and these change quite a bit from time to time. (Another complication is that what I regard as a comfortable temperature also varies since it depends on the outside temperature and on what I have been doing, but let's leave that complication out.) So how do I control the system? I do what I expect everyone else does, I turn on the taps to some midway position and put my hand into the water stream to 'see' (*sense* is the technical term) what the water temperature is. If the water is too hot I adjust the taps in the appropriate manner and sample the water again. I repeat this process of sampling or sensing the water temperature and making adjustments to the inputs until my goal state is achieved. If you have ever tried to do this you may have found that it is not quite as simple as this. I shall go into the reasons for this later.

This kind of control method, where the current value of the output of the system is sensed by someone or something, and the information thus obtained used to make appropriate adjustments to the inputs, is called *feedback control*. The output value is compared with the desired or required value and the difference is used or *fed back* to make adjustments to the control inputs, hence *feedback control*. In my earlier example of open loop control the actions on the system, or more correctly on the inputs, were decided beforehand and without reference to the actual current output.

feedback control

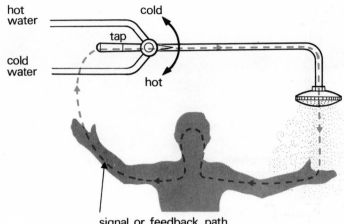

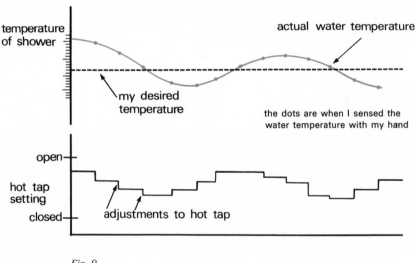

*Fig. 9*

If you look at the diagram of the shower system (Fig. 9) you will see that there is a connection or link running between the output and input via me. This link forms part of a complete circuit which goes right round the system. This circuit is called a *loop* and so the control method I employed is known as *closed loop control*. Now you can see why the other method I discussed before is called open loop: the 'loop' is not complete, it is open.

closed loop control

Closed loop or feedback control is of tremendous importance in engineering and we shall be devoting a complete unit to control later in the course. The earliest recorded example* of feedback control is a furnace control device invented by Cornelius Drebbel sometime in the early 1600s. This was a simple kind of thermostat for opening and closing a furnace damper as the temperature of the furnace rose or fell. A little later, about 1713, one Humphrey Potter became famous in the history of control devices. Potter was an attendant on one of Newcomen's atmospheric steam engines. These worked by letting steam into a large cylinder, making the

---

* Self-regulatory devices were in use as early as 247 BC but Drebbel's device is probably the first true self-regulating system. See Mayr, O. (1971) *The origins of feedback control*, MIT Press.

steam condense by spraying in cold water, and allowing the partial vacuum formed to cause atmospheric pressure to be exerted on a piston. You can see how the engine worked from the diagram in Fig 10.

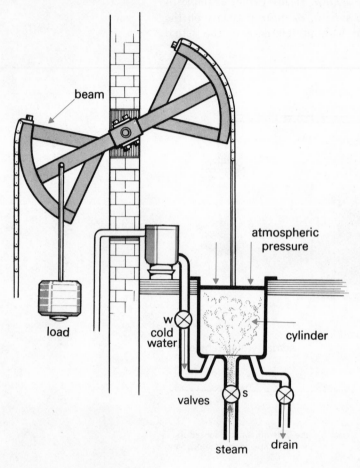

*Fig. 10   Newcomen's atmospheric engine.*

The attendant's job was to operate the valves which let the steam and water into the cylinder. The sequence was:

(1)   Let steam in by opening valve S.
(2)   When the cylinder was full of steam, close S and let water spray in by opening valve W.
(3)   Close the water valve as the piston descended and then open valve S again to restart the cycle.

This cycle had to be repeated all the time to make the beam go up and down. Humphrey decided that he could save himself some work by making the beam operate the valves itself as it went up and down. So he arranged a link to the two valves so that as the beam descended it began to open the steam valve, and as it started upwards it eventually opened the water valve. So long as steam came from the boiler the engine would work itself. It is not recorded what Humphrey did while this was happening.

**Example 12**

Have a look at the diagram in Fig. 10 again and decide whether the control system is open or closed loop.

For answer, see end of unit.

Later still in the eighteenth century James Watt invented the steam governor which worked by sensing the speed of an engine shaft and used this value to adjust the steam flow which drove the engine so that the engine speed was controlled to within fairly close limits. It was nearly 100 years later before James Clerk Maxwell worked out the mathematical laws which describe the behaviour of this device. The Watt governor is still used today in some car engines to actuate various mechanisms which must be related to engine speed, for example, the timing of the spark to the cylinder.

Feedback loops occur in many natural systems and act so as to regulate the behaviour of these systems. Notice I have said regulate rather than control, because no man is deciding on this control: it occurs as a natural consequence of the arrangement of the system. A good example is the regulation of predator–prey populations. If we have a limited territory containing a number of prey and a number of predators, the respective numbers may fluctuate in a cyclic manner. This happens because, say at first the predators find plenty of prey, then they can multiply and grow; the larger numbers of these predators rapidly reduce the population of prey, so the predators begin to die off because they cannot get enough to eat. As the predator population declines, the few remaining prey have a chance to reproduce and increase again, and so the cycle repeats itself. Some population fluctuations are shown in Figs. 11 and 12.

population changes

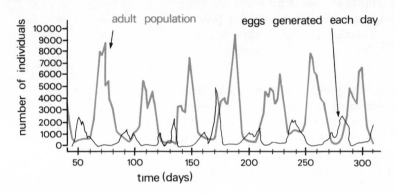

*Fig. 11   Numbers of the blowfly* Lucilia *in a population cage. Larvae received unlimited food, and adults received a limited supply of 0·5g of liver daily. (After Nicholson, A. J. (1954), Aust. J. Zool.* **2**, *9.)*

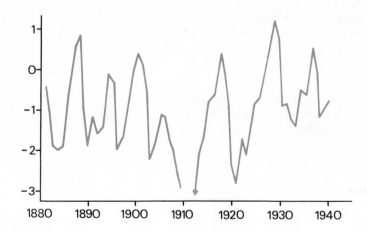

*Fig. 12   Fluctuations in the numbers of the moth* Bupalus *in pine forests in Germany, on a logarithmic scale. The ordinate is* $\log_{10}x$ *where* x *is the number of pupae per* $m^2$. *Thus there are fluctuations of the order of a thousand-fold in density, with a periodicity of about 6 years prior to 1906, and a somewhat longer period subsequently. Parasitism may be part of the explanation for these oscillations. (After Varley, G. C. (1949), J. Anim. Ecol.* **18**, *117.)*

> Can you draw a graph of the possible changes in the populations of a predator and a prey? Start with equal numbers and go through several cycles.

There is, incidentally, a good example here of what taking a systems approach means in this predator–prey situation. Mankind has tried to eliminate certain animals because they are a nuisance to him and he has found some very effective poisons. He applies these, with the result that the unwanted animal's population declines rapidly. While he is congratulating himself, the prey of that declining animal is busily multiplying away with nothing left to stop it. To his horror, mankind now finds itself knee-deep in another undesirable animal, the prey! Hopefully a systems approach would have drawn attention to the interrelations between populations of animals and their food supplies and the extent of the system might have been revealed at the start.

I want to go back now to one point about my shower (Fig. 9). Why is it sometimes difficult to exercise feedback control in these situations? The reason is similar to the one which causes the cycling up and down of the predator–prey populations. It is because it takes time for the effects of changes to the inputs of a system to reach the outputs. The water coming into the taps takes a little while to reach the shower head and to come down to me. If the water coming out is too hot, the admission of more cold water and less hot will not immediately produce colder water. The pipes have to cool down a little, but more important the colder mixture has to travel from the valves to me. This takes time. I get impatient while waiting for this to happen and I try to hurry the process up. The result is that I turn the taps too far first in one direction and then in the other. You see the same effect sometimes when a learner driver is learning to steer a car.

Perhaps the graph in Fig. 9 will make the problem clearer to you. This time delay between the moment of operating the controls and the effect appearing in the output of the system is called *lag*. In the case of my shower the lag is mostly due to the time taken for the new mixture of hot and cold water to reach me from the valve. Lags of this kind are quite common in industrial systems and they are sometimes called *transport* lags, or *distance–velocity* lags. lag transport lags

Another kind of lag which occurs frequently and is perhaps more difficult to explain than a transport lag is the *exponential* lag. This lag effect occurs very widely in mechanical, hydraulic and electrical systems. One way to illustrate it is to use water flow into and out of tanks because this is easy to visualize and much the same effects occur with the flow of electricity. Imagine a tank like the one in Fig. 13 which, say, is used to allow something to settle out of a liquid flow. The rate ($v$) at which the water flows out of the outlet pipe depends only on the size of the pipe, which is fixed, and the height of liquid in the tank. If there is no liquid coming into the tank (valve A: closed), then the flow out will start at a high rate and as the level falls it will slow down and down until it eventually stops altogether. I have plotted the flow rate against time in Fig. 13. exponential lag

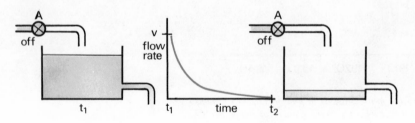

*Fig. 13*

Now suppose the system is working continuously and liquid is flowing into the tank via valve A and out again through the outlet. The height of water will rise to a level where the output flow is equal to the input flow.

$$v_{in} = v_{out}.$$

Suppose that now we want to cut down the flow out to a slower rate. Well, we close valve A a little, but what happens to the flow out? See Fig. 14.

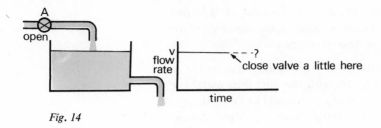

*Fig. 14*

Eventually the flow out reaches a new lower rate, but it takes some time for the level in the tank to fall to a new steady height. The change looks something like that shown in Fig. 15.

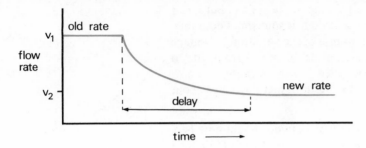

*Fig. 15*

You can see that there is a delay between the altering of valve A and the new steady flow rate. This is due to the tank emptying out to the new level and it follows a similar curve to the straightforward emptying shown in Fig. 13. When the valve is opened a similar effect, but in reverse, occurs (see Fig. 16).

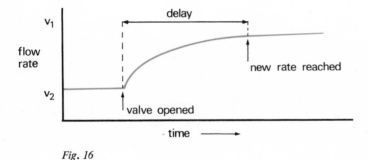

*Fig. 16*

These lags are very common and they have one feature of particular interest: the approach to the new steady rate becomes imperceptibly slower and slower—in fact it is difficult to say exactly when the new rate is actually reached. The mathematical form of this curve is called an exponential, hence exponential lag, and you will become more familiar with it as you study this and other courses in Science and Technology.

The behaviour of closed-loop systems which have a method of *feeding back* information to affect the input to the system can be very complex. We shall take up the different kinds of behaviour in detail in later units, particularly in Unit 16, Control, but it is worth making a few points here.

Feedback can be of two kinds, *positive* and *negative*. These are in fact quite complex processes but they can be understood as follows: with *positive* feedback, if the system output increases, the feedback message acts on the input to cause the system to *increase further* its output. Similarly, if the output decreases, then feedback which causes further decrease in the output is also positive. Negative feedback acts the *opposite* way: if the output increases, then the feedback causes the system to react by reducing its output and vice versa.

Feedback systems can behave in a variety of ways depending on whether the feedback is negative or positive, and also on the kind of lags and connections which exist within the system. Characteristic behaviours are often seen, however, and these are of several kinds.

The system's output can tend towards some steady-state value and stay there. For example, if you look at Fig. 14, with the inlet flow matching the outlet flow the system output of *height of water* would be fairly steady. If the inlet flow is changed our system's output (height) would change towards a new steady level.

In other cases a system's output can be variable, that is, not tend towards any steady-state value. The output can fluctuate from one extreme value to another or cycle up and down as did the temperature of my shower, shown in Fig. 9. It is caused in this case by a lag in the system, but it can arise from other causes. This fluctuating behaviour is sometimes desirable, as in an electronic oscillator, where we want a cyclic variation in voltage or current, or undesirable, as when a learner driver moves from side to side down the road. This latter is often called *hunting* because we know the system output should be a steady value but it in fact fluctuates about this desired value.

hunting

We shall go into this further later in the course but you should note here that *in general* negative feedback systems provide a means of obtaining a steady system output whereas positive feedback systems are often unstable or lead to oscillations (hunting) which we may or may not want.

Section 10

# Self-controlling systems

The topics of lags and control will be taken up again in later units in our course but there is one further aspect I want to deal with here, and that concerns the question of automatic control. The Watt governor is an example of self-regulation where a machine has the means, to some extent, to regulate its *own* behaviour. Feedback control systems have been developed enormously since Watt's time and there are now very sophisticated control systems available for industrial processes and for aircraft, rockets and guided missiles. An oil refinery, for example, operates today almost entirely under 'self' control with many hundreds of feedback loops regulating the different functions in the processes. The development of these control devices has led to a large body of engineering and mathematical theory to cope with the properties and behaviour of these systems. Even so, there are still many properties of control systems which cannot yet be readily analysed.

Quite early in the development of these automatic control devices the similarity of their behaviour became obvious and naturally aroused a great deal of speculation and interest in the idea that human behaviour could be the result of feedback control systems. (Clearly though, they would be very complex ones.) As is often the case, early enthusiasm for this idea became moderated when attempts were made to build machines to behave as human beings do in fact behave. It was soon discovered that biological systems possessed properties which seemed impossible to duplicate and it is still a source of great controversy as to whether we can understand and copy human thinking and behaviour on the basis of automatic control theory and cybernetic ideas, or whether we are on the wrong track entirely and some other quite different mechanisms or methods exist in brains. Many attempts have been made to build thinking machines, self-controlling machines, self-organizing machines and so on, and certainly some of the devices which have been constructed behave in very interesting and subtle ways. However, it seems to me that even the best of these do little more than mirror some rather simple aspects of human behaviour.

Some would claim that more success has been achieved using computer simulations of behaviour: computer programs in computers can now be programmed to play games of draughts and chess quite well. Some of these programs include methods by which the computer can learn, that is modify its behaviour in the light of experience; these programs are usually called adaptive programs.

These two approaches, feedback systems and computer program simulations, are still being actively studied but there is a third school of thought which is exploring the idea of trying to get a 'machine' to develop its own intelligence or behaviour. The idea behind this is to some extent based on the properties of complex systems. The argument runs that as the complexity of a system increases, so do the range and variety of its behaviours. We have already seen how large the possible behaviours of quite small systems can become. So it could be, the argument goes, that there is nothing special about biological systems and the remarkable properties we associate with living things are just the outcome of the interactions between the vast numbers of components involved. This idea has led to attempts to build up networks of simple units which are allowed to develop their own interconnections. These units are often based on logic gates which behave in a rudimentary way like nerve cells. So far relatively little has emerged from this kind of research and the attempts to copy brain-type circuitry are hampered by our lack of knowledge about the brain as well as by the complexity of the nerve cell's actual operation.

One outcome of this work may be discoveries about how the brain performs some of its most remarkable functions so that we can copy the techniques in our engineering systems. The brain has the ability to recognize patterns, to learn, to adapt to new circumstances, and to cope with a tremendous variety of situations. These would be very useful properties in engineering mechanisms if we could find out how to copy them. For this reason some engineers are turning to new areas of research in fields like artificial intelligence, bio-engineering, pattern and speech recognition, and so on, in the hope of learning how the biological system does it all.

The field of self-organizing systems and artificial intelligence is growing rapidly and it would take us too far away from our main theme to explore it further here. There are some references at the end of this unit for you to follow up if you are interested.

**Section 11**

# The systems approach

An awareness of systems concepts and ideas is undoubtedly of some value in itself to anyone concerned with real-world situations, which indeed applies to all of us. But it would be of much greater value if we had a more formal method of applying systems ideas to real-world problems which would lead to solutions. At the present time we have gone some way to establishing a more formal method, a systems methodology in fact, but by no means *all* the way. This idea of a methodology is usually described in terms of something called the *systems approach* and it is important to realize that it is not a *technique*, that is, something which if you apply it correctly will inevitably lead to an answer.

Procedures of this kind, which if followed step by step *must* lead to an end result (and usually a solution) are called *algorithms*. There is, for example, an algorithm for the game of noughts and crosses which if applied correctly means that you cannot lose a game. You cannot ensure winning but you will *always* draw or win if you use the algorithm. Fortunately there is no algorithm for chess, even for computers playing chess, so there is room for human skill, which is what makes the game still worth playing. Non-algorithmic procedures which nevertheless work well or are powerful in getting good results some of the time are called *heuristic* procedures. Human beings are remarkably good at finding or developing heuristic procedures, in fact we are probably the only systems which can do this.

To some extent present developments of the systems approach are heuristic procedures—they assist us to tackle real-world problems but they do *not* provide Royal roads to *the* correct answer. I would also remind you that at the beginning of this unit I drew attention to the fact that there is an individual element in the very definition of a system to study. The applier of systems ideas brings his or her viewpoint into the situation, so there is inevitably a diffuse area where the individual's purpose, values, opinions and attitudes enter to some extent into the situation. I would even go further and say that there is an intuitive element in applying systems ideas. Somewhere in the approach, whether the aim is a systems analysis, design, or redesign, the systems man will reach a point where there are no further rules to follow and there has to be a search for possible solutions or ideas to meet particular needs. This process is similar to problem solving: we follow a set procedure if we have one, but we nearly always reach a point where it is just not clear what to do next. Most of us then hunt around, more or less at random, hoping to hit on some useful idea. We know very little about the internal brain processes involved in these searches but you will certainly have had the experience of suddenly seeing a connection, or a possible solution which you can try. Sometimes the whole answer appears in a flash, as when you finish a jigsaw or crossword puzzle in an inspired gallop.

One of the merits of a systems approach is that it provides a flexible tool for tackling all kinds of situations and that it does at least identify the points at which some original thinking is required and other points where established methods can be used. It should not be surprising that it is a general-purpose tool because one of the main points of this unit has been to try to show you that everything is a system, or rather can be treated as one.

What then can be said about a systems approach? Many textbooks offer methods for carrying out a systems analysis or a systems design but generally speaking they do not help very much since they either deal only with rather specific cases—for example, systems analysis usually deals with specialized computer-based systems—or with very general cases where they offer advice such as 'draw the appropriate systems boundaries' without giving you any guidance as to how to interpret 'appropriate'.

Probably the most helpful approach is the one developed by Professor Jenkins* and his colleagues in the Systems Engineering Department at Lancaster University. The following description is taken from one of Professor Checkland's papers:

The Systems Engineer is concerned with four stages of a systems study:

> 1. *Systems Analysis* including problem formulation
> 2. *Systems Design*
> 3. *Implementation* of the proposed design
> 4. *Operation* and subsequent *reappraisal*

(1.) *Systems Analysis including problem formulation*

If the system is a new one, to perform a new function, then 'the problem' is to create a system to achieve the stated objective. More often than not, however, the Systems Engineer is working in an existing situation in which 'a problem' is thought to reside. Even if 'the problem' is presented in clear-cut terms, the Systems Engineer does not accept the statement of it without deeper investigation. *The most difficult part of the Systems Engineer's job is seeking out and defining 'the problem', and stating it in systems terms in a structured way which allows a rational approach to solution.* It is more difficult than creating a solution because help in the latter is usually available in the form of standard techniques and written-up examples of their use; whereas defining *a structured problem from an unstructured situation* is often a unique operation without precedent.

The Systems Engineer's approach at this stage; and an appropriate sequence in which to examine the problem situation, is summarised below.

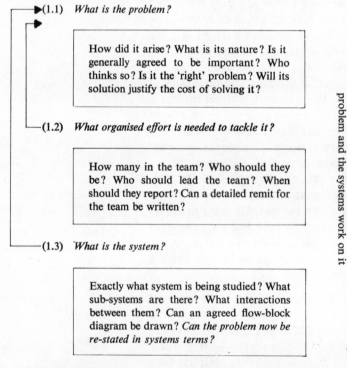

(1.1) *What is the problem?*

> How did it arise? What is its nature? Is it generally agreed to be important? Who thinks so? Is it the 'right' problem? Will its solution justify the cost of solving it?

(1.2) *What organised effort is needed to tackle it?*

> How many in the team? Who should they be? Who should lead the team? When should they report? Can a detailed remit for the team be written?

(1.3) *What is the system?*

> Exactly what system is being studied? What sub-systems are there? What interactions between them? Can an agreed flow-block diagram be drawn? *Can the problem now be re-stated in systems terms?*

Continuing dialogue with management on the problem and the systems work on it

* Jenkins, G.M. (1969) 'The systems approach', *Journal of systems engineering*, **1**, (1), reprinted in Beishon, R. J. and Peters, G. (eds.) (1972) *Systems behaviour*, Open University Press/Harper & Row.

(1.4) *What are the wider systems?*

In what environment does the system operate? What are the links between the system and the wider systems of which it is a part? Are there effects from any yet-wider systems which must be taken into account?

(1.5) *What are the objectives of the wider systems?*

Have the higher systems in the hierarchy been taken into account? What is the influence of the wider systems on the system being studied? What must be taken into account to prevent sub-optimising the system?

(1.6) *What are the objectives of the system?*

Can they be clearly stated, and agreed by the team and management? Can they be placed in order of importance? Can the constraints be identified? Are they compatible with the wider systems' objectives? Can they be quantified? Can an economic criterion which expresses the system's objectives be defined?

(1.7) *What are the measures of performance?*

Can conflicting objectives be properly weighted? What are the constraints? Are criteria and constraints as simple and direct as possible? Can they be agreed, even if qualitative?

(1.8) *What data and information must be collected?*

What data will be needed for any system modelling? Is it available? Who has it? Who should collect it? How can it best be presented? What is its reliability?

Iteration as necessary

Continuing dialogue with management on the problem and the systems work on it

Four important points must be made about this stage.

—In the sequence above we have a sequence of considerations which must be examined together: that is the meaning of the iterations. It will always be wrong to expect that 'What is the problem?' can be answered once and for all before moving on to 'What is the system?' etc. In this sequence each set of answers will tend to modify the answers already obtained. A final set of answers to all the questions 1.1 to 1.8 *will require several iterations,* and the final picture of 'the problem in systems terms' will be the result of assessment of intangibles as well as the result of answering the formal questions.

—Note that in the sequence

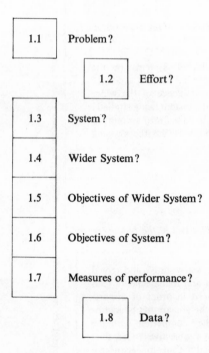

| 1.1 | Problem? |
| 1.2 | Effort? |
| 1.3 | System? |
| 1.4 | Wider System? |
| 1.5 | Objectives of Wider System? |
| 1.6 | Objectives of System? |
| 1.7 | Measures of performance? |
| 1.8 | Data? |

items 1.2 and 1.8 are different in kind from the other considerations. The other questions refer to the intellectual structure of the problem, but 1.2 and 1.8 are highly practical considerations which could themselves force a redefinition of the problem to be tackled, of the system to be engineered. Lack of the necessary effort, or lack of data, could both reduce the scope of the problem finally tackled.

—As important as the iterations is the need for the whole of this first stage to be carried out in continuous dialogue with management. Their commitment will derive only from their involvement.

—Finally it is worth emphasising the least formalised part of this stage: it is 1.3–1.6. In choosing 'the system', which we shall proceed to design in stage 2, we are defining also what level we shall call a 'sub-system' and what level is the 'wider system'.

No doubt more formal methods will be developed in the future, but at present this is an intuitive judgement aided by the answers to all the questions listed.

(2.) *Systems Design*

At the end of stage 1 there should be a structured problem, in systems terms, and agreed criteria for judging improvement; data should be available for design purposes, but obviously further information may have to be collected during subsequent phases.

**Iteration as necessary**

**(2.1)** *Forecasting*

What will the future of the system and its environment be? Is there guaranteed continuity? Is there data available for accurate forecasts? How accurate?

**(2.2)** *Model Building*

What kind of model, if any, is needed? Are the objectives of model building clear? Is the model as simple as possible? Is model building compatible with project timing as in 1.2? Are potential users involved? Does the model adequately describe the real situation? Does any simulated performance agree with actual past performance or future conjectured performance? Is the model good enough for attempts at optimisation?

**(2.3)** *Optimisation*

How should the model(s) be optimised: what technique? If optimisation is not formal, how can alternatives be generated? Are the criteria for showing improvement sufficiently sensitive? Has optimised performance been checked against assumptions?

**(2.4)** *Control*

What control system is needed to achieve and maintain the optimised conditions? Is it economic relative to the improvement it secures? What form of control system is needed? Instrumentation? Reports? Is the control system as simple as possible?

**(2.5)** *Reliability*

Has the uncertainty (unpredictable events) been taken into account? What extra standby equipment or manpower is needed? At what cost? Can the system afford it? Can further simulation (perhaps with a modified model) check reliability? What can be done to improve reliability? Finally, has unreliability been reduced to an acceptable level?

**Continuing dialogue with management on the problem and the systems work on it**

Three points must be made about the Systems Design stage.

—If it is possible to make use of specialists during any of this stage, especially during 2.2, *then do so without hesitation*. But *do not let any specialist model builder become dominant*, since model building as a technique involving quantifiable variables has been developed far beyond our ability to represent factors—frequently psychological or political—which in real-life situations are crucial.

—Do not be surprised if a model representing flows of money, materials, information etc. cannot be built. 'Modelling' covers a wide span of activities and stretches from drawing conceptual diagrams to programming sets of equations for computers. Even if the latter is possible, the former must be well done first—and in many real-life situations it is the only modelling which is justified.

—Thirdly it is worth emphasising the obvious need for management involvement in this phase of the systems work. Not only must assumptions in modelling be checked with managers but also it is vital to obtain their agreement on what is possible, within the situation as it exists, in the areas of control and reliability.

(3.) *Implementation of the proposed design*

Too many 'management scientists' see their role as that of a planner who operates away from the problem situation but finally emerges from his lair with 'the solution' which line management should implement. It is far better that the Systems Engineer should be closely involved in the working situation throughout the systems study and should ensure a continuing dialogue with management throughout the work. Also the Systems Engineer should if possible be 'ready, willing and anxious' to take part in the implementation stage. It is at this stage that his skill as a communicator is most needed.

(3.1) *Documentation and Sanctions*

Does the team agree the conclusions? Have they been communicated to management (a) verbally, (b) in well-written reports? Is there agreement on implementation? A time-table for it? Do all the people concerned really understand what has been done and what is proposed?

(3.2) *Construction* (Installation)

Has the system been specified down to the small details of equipment and procedures? Is there a schedule for building and implementation? Do those installing the system understand enough of the background?

Continuing dialogue with management

Perhaps the most important point to make about this stage concerns 3.1. In order to avoid the frustration of finding out at this late stage that management does not agree with something basic in the Analysis or Design stages, *work towards 3.1 must begin early.*

Brief, cogent, well-written reports should be written during stages 1 and 2, so that when the specific proposals emerge in 3.1, the way for them has been well-prepared. Any idea that a 'deus ex machina' at this stage will be greeted with cries of delight is totally wrong.

(4.) *Operation and subsequent reappraisal*

After design, construction and installation comes a moment of truth: how does it operate? Here again the Systems Engineer should be closely involved, and should ensure close liaison between users and systems team. If there has not been a user in the team itself, one should certainly join it before reaching stage 4. If possible the users should learn about the system from one of their own colleagues, someone they know and trust. The Systems Engineer can afford to be self-effacing during this stage!

Subsequently, it is important to review actual against predicted performance (though this is often neglected) and to re-optimise or re-design if necessary.

(4.1)  *Initial Operation*

> Is there a start-up plan? How exactly will hand-over occur? Are responsibilities defined at each stage? Do the users believe it will be possible to operate the system? Is the method for documenting the initial operation agreed?

(4.2)  *Retrospective Appraisal*

> Does actual performance agree with that predicted? If not, why not? Exactly what went wrong? What needs further attention?

(4.3)  *Improved Operation*

> Is further systems work necessary? Re-optimising? Re-training? Re-design? If so, how should it be done?
>
> Finally: is the now-improved performance adequate?

*Continuing dialogue with management*

There is one important point to make about this stage: 'No recriminations' is a popular cry, but for a systems engineer anxious to learn from his experience this time, in order to do better next, retrospective appraisal must not be neglected.

Jenkins's systems approach has been successfully applied to 'hard' systems which can be said to have a relatively clear-cut set of objectives but when we come to 'softer' social or organizational systems, this approach has limitations. Professor P. B. Checkland at Lancaster has begun the process of developing a 'softer' systems methodology* but it would take us too far into the details of systems methodologies to deal with it here.

You will find the above approach useful for many of the situations you will meet in later units in this course but I would like to add one further aid in the form of a list of systems questions† which will prove valuable for organizing your thoughts about a topic under study.

(1)  Why are we studying the system?
(2)  What kind of system is it?
(3)  What is its goal/purpose?
(4)  What constitutes the system:
     (a) Components/subsystems, (b) boundaries?
(5)  What constitutes the systems environment? What are the systems inputs and outputs and interaction with this environment and other systems?
(6)  Identification and measurement of systems variables.
(7)  How does the system operate:
     response to inputs, speed and flexibility of response?
(8)  Systems response to abnormal inputs, reaction to component breakdowns and/or failure.
(9)  Future changes in the system.

You will find it a useful exercise to apply these questions to case studies described in the book of the course *The man-made world*.

* Checkland P. B. (1973) *'Towards a systems-based methodology for real-world problem solving,' Journal of systems engineering*, **3**, (2).

† First suggested by Peter Zorkoczy of the course team.

## 11.1 System design

How you start using the systems approach depends on what you are aiming to do. If you are starting from scratch to design a new system you will begin by setting out the objectives, goals and aims of the exercise. You will then have to draw up a tentative boundary to your system. I say tentative because one of the key points worth restating is that using a systems approach involves a constant cycling around the procedures to redefine the problem or to make adjustments to previous decisions. Professor Neil has drawn attention to this very clearly in his paper* and the process is known as *iteration*, the repeated movement around a loop of procedures until you reach a satisfactory state or conclusion so that you can go on to a next step.

iteration

Having settled on a boundary and a set of terms of reference, you can start to think of possible sub-systems and their interrelationships. In designing new things, however, it may be undesirable to set boundaries within which to operate, it may be desirable or even essential to go outside the initial constraints and to redefine the whole problem. Some of the most successful and dramatic solutions to problems have emerged from refusals to accept conventional restraints. We have a complete sub-system on design at the end of our foundation course so I am not going to follow up these points any further here.

The feasibility of the sub-systems must be established and where snags emerge, the previous steps will have to be repeated or iterated until feasible sub-systems do appear.

Now the interactions between the sub-systems must be modelled. Sometimes mathematical techniques are available which enable one to calculate what will happen to the larger system when the sub-systems interact in all the possible ways, but usually real systems are too complex for this, even if simplifying assumptions are made. The alternatives are to deal only with likely possibilities or to model the system either in real hardware like a plane in a wind tunnel, or as a computer model of the variables. You can then switch on the machine or computer, set up various sub-system states, and let the thing run and watch what happens. The results of this kind of investigation will almost certainly send you back round the iterative loop again.

Your next step is to settle on the sub-systems and then to begin to look at the sub-sub-systems. The decision as to how far down the sub-sub-system path one must travel is difficult and seems at the moment to be one of those intuitive points I mentioned earlier. But having made a decision, however arbitrary, these sub-sub-system interactions must be examined. Again you may find that the lower level may change your sub-systems behaviour and you will have to return to higher levels again.

Eventually you should reach a sub-sub-etc.-system level where it becomes clear that lower sub-systems are not going to be able (or are very unlikely) to affect your main sub-systems, and you can stop.

The whole system then has to be realized or constructed and tested.

## 11.2 System analysis

If you are primarily concerned with system analysis you will probably start from a problem. The existing system is failing to achieve its objectives or it has developed a fault. The problem must be looked at carefully to see first of all whether it really is the kind of problem it seems to be. It could be that the apparent fault or failure is actually due to the system

* Appendix 2.

50

operating in a perfectly normal but unusual mode. You would not find a faulty component or a failed interconnection in such a system, no matter how hard you looked. Remember this when you study the north-east American power failure in the Systems File.

Having decided what kind of status your problem has, keeping reservations, of course, you can then proceed both inwards into the sub-systems and outwards into the environment. You will try to identify the sub-systems and their interrelations, and begin to build up a structure of the system. Where you get stuck you will postulate a sub-system and define possible functions. Later you can try working your model of the system and the value of your guesses or postulates will appear. You work at one level at a time only going into more detailed sub-systems as the need arises.

Your look outwards into the system environment is to see if there are any feedback loops outside your system which come back into it at a lower and possibly unexpected sub-system level. Many commercial and industrial systems have been shown to be unstable or suicidal because links back to the system were not discovered or even suspected. With economic systems, governments (and economists) seem constantly to be surprised at the peculiar effects of their decisions which are often very unexpected. They are just not able to see how some of their changes go out of the system and reappear again in an unexpected quarter. To be fair, economic systems are extremely complicated, possibly the most complicated systems we try to control apart from biological systems and these, fortunately for us, have this self-controlling property.

The system analysis will be complete when you have discovered enough about the system to be able to predict its behaviour (unless your aim was scientific and analytical so you would still want to know exactly *how* it worked).

One interesting aside here—we seem to do very well at controlling the behaviour of biological systems without knowing very much about how they or their sub-systems work. Training of animals, for example, is not very difficult and we can get animals to do astonishing things. Trainers in circuses adopt a very 'high level' systems approach. They experiment or use the results of years of experience (i.e. another name for observation and experimentation) to find simple and effective training procedures. They do not worry about how the animal's brain works—they rely on input–output connections being established. Maybe we could achieve better control of our economy with a little of this kind of experimentation at a high level but, of course, one of the major difficulties with economic systems is that there are so many inputs and outputs to relate, so perhaps this would not be very practicable.

System analysis and design are still a little like swimming. You can be instructed again and again in the appropriate motions but when you finally get into the water you are on your own and everyone has to learn to swim for himself. You will learn the systems approach by trying to do it.

## 11.3 Final comment

I have now reached the end of this first unit. To go on now would take us into the subject matter of the many other units you are going to get in this course, where the topics are dealt with in more detail. I am already in trouble with my colleagues for encroaching on their more specialized ground and this is a characteristic situation for the systems man. He does not have specific subject or discipline boundaries. He is concerned just as much with computer systems as transport systems, with production systems as biological systems, with control systems as organizational systems, with economic systems as with educational systems. So I hope that you will now be able to look at the world, and yourself, from a slightly different viewpoint—a systems viewpoint.

To give you some idea of how the systems approach can be applied I have reproduced in Appendix 2 extracts from an article by Professor M. W. Neil, who applied these ideas to the design of the Open University.

# Suggestions for further reading

Ashby, R. (1958.) *Introduction to cybernetics* John Wiley.

Ashby, R. (1952.) *Design for a brain* Chapman and Hall.

Beer, S. (1966.) *Decision and control* John Wiley.

Beishon, R. J. and Peters, G. (eds.) (1972.) *Systems behaviour* Open University Press/Harper and Row.

Bertalanffy, L. von (1968.) *General system theory* George Braziller.

Buckley, W. (1967.) *Sociology and modern systems theory* Prentice-Hall.

Coombs, P. H. (1968.) *The world educational crisis: a systems analysis* Oxford University Press.

Emery, F. E. (ed.) (1969.) *Systems thinking*. Penguin Books.

Hall, A. D. (1962.) *A methodology for systems engineering* Van Nostrand.

Katz, D. and Kahn, R. L. (1966.) *The social psychology of organizations* John Wiley.

Mesarovič, D. (ed.) (1964.) *Views on general sytems theory* John Wiley.

Porter, A. (1969.) *Cybernetics simplified* English Universities Press.

Rose, J. (1969.) *Survey of cybernetics* Iliffe Books.

Wiener, N. (1961.) *Cybernetics* MIT Press.

## Exercises on exponents

You will soon get used to dealing with numbers like this: $10^5$ or $3^4$. Remember that the little number above the main number tells you how many times the main number is multiplied by itself. So $3 \times 3 = 3^2$ (we say this as—'three squared') and $5 \times 5 \times 5 = 3^3$ ('five cubed') and $10^5 = 10 \times 10 \times 10 \times 10 \times 10$ ('ten to the fifth').

Now do these:

1   $2 \times 2 \times 2 \times 2 = 2^?$
2   $5 \times 5 \times 5 = 5^?$
3   $6 \times 6 = 6^?$
4   $14 \times 14 \times 14 = 14^?$
5   $17 \times 17 \times 17 \times 17 = 17^?$
6   $5^4 = ?$ write out in full, e.g. $5^2 = 5 \times 5 = 25$
7   $10^4 = ?$
8   $17^4 = ?$
9   $2^6 = ?$
10   $9^3 = ?$
11   $x^3 = ?$
12   $y^4 = ?$

Notice that anything 'multiplied' by itself only once equals itself, that is $10^1 = 10$ and $4^1 = 4$.

The fact that our normal everyday number system is in tens means that we can write numbers like this:

$200 = 2 \times 100 = 2 \times 10 \times 10 = 2 \times 10^2$
$14\,000 = 14 \times 1\,000 = 14 \times 10 \times 10 \times 10 = 14 \times 10^3$
$4\,000\,000 = 4 \times 1\,000\,000 = 4 \times 10 \times 10 \times 10 \times 10 \times 10 \times 10 = 4 \times 10^6$

You will soon get to know that $10^2 = 100$
$$10^3 = 1\,000$$
$$10^6 = 1\,000\,000$$

We can write numbers such as $1\,732.000$ as $\dfrac{17\,320}{10}$ or $173.2 \times 10$ if we like.

This means that we can put $1\,732.000$ in several ways.

$1\,73.2 \ \times 10$
$17.32 \ \ \times 100$
or   $1.732 \ \ \times 1\,000$
or even   $0.173\,2 \times 10\,000$

And we can use our exponent notation to write this number as:

$173.2 \ \ \times 10^1$
or   $17.32 \ \ \times 10^2$
or   $1.732 \ \ \times 10^3$
or   $0.173\,2 \times 10^4$

Try these examples:

13   $224 = 22.4 \times 10^?$
14   $22.4 = 0.224 \times 10^?$

15     $22.4 \times 10^3 = ?$

16     $0.224 \times 10^4 = ?$

17     $224\,000 = 2.24 \times ?$

18     $17\,320 = 1.732 \times ?$

19     $169.45 \times 10^6 = ?$

20     $1.924 \times 10^3 = ?$

In a similar way it is often convenient to write numbers smaller than 1 like this:

$$\frac{1}{200} = \frac{1}{2 \times 100} = \frac{1}{2 \times 10 \times 10} = \frac{1}{2 \times 10^2}$$

$$\text{and } \frac{1}{1\,000} = \frac{1}{10 \times 10 \times 10} = \frac{1}{10^3}$$

This form of fraction is a nuisance to write or print and it is generally easier to write it on one line. To do this we use a simple convention—we write $\frac{1}{10}$ as $10^{-1}$ and $\frac{1}{100}$ as $10^{-2}$ and so on.

So our examples above can be written

$$\frac{1}{2 \times 10^2} = \frac{1}{2} \times 10^{-2} \text{ or } 0.5 \times 10^{-2}$$

$$\frac{1}{10^3} = 10^{-3}$$

We can also write $\frac{1}{10}$ as 0.1 and $\frac{1}{10^2}$ as 0.01 and so on.

$10^{-3}$ is therefore 0.001.

Now try these:

21     $\dfrac{1}{10^4} = 10^?$

22     $0.001 = \dfrac{1}{?}$

23     $\dfrac{1}{2\,000} = \dfrac{1}{2} \times 10^?$

24     $0.5 \times 10^{-2} = \dfrac{1}{?}$

25     $\dfrac{1}{14} \times 10^{-3} = \dfrac{1}{?}$

26     $\dfrac{1}{24} \times 10^{-2} = \dfrac{1}{?}$

27     $1.73 \times 10^{-3} = ?$

28     $6.82 \times 10^{-3} = ?$

29     $7.49 \times 10^{-2} = ?$

30     $168.32 \times 10^{-1} = ?$

31     $1.01 \times 10^{-6} = ?$

32     $70.6 \times 10^{-1} = ?$

33     $\dfrac{1}{1.001 \times 10^3} = \dfrac{1}{?} \times 10^{-2}$

34     $\dfrac{1}{40\,000} = 0.25 \times ?$

# The Open University system

This is an interesting system to study, since you are familiar with it, or soon will be, and it was carefully planned from a systems point of view. The material which follows is taken from a paper by Professor M. W. Neil who is a consultant to the Open University and who was engaged in the initial planning.

It is, I believe, extremely important to distinguish between a 'systematic' and a 'systems' approach. The diagram referred to (Fig. 17) is largely a 'systematic' approach with only hints of a 'systems' approach, interpreted as one which uses the concepts of cybernetics and general systems theory as bases for systems design. In practice, from hard experience, when it is required to convince those who are not familiar with systems ideas, it is best to proceed with a systematic approach first, using a minimum of technical jargon, and only at later stages to more sophisticated ideas which may present very real problems in communication.

We ask 'what system and why are we concerned with it?' In the present instance no 'system' existed. The Open University challenge is that of creating a new system. Consequently, we first built a simple model of the University's main functional activity areas (Fig. 18). From this model we derived a primary functional activity in more detail which represented the essential processes for creating, preparing, producing and disseminating materials for students.

Associated with this activity are a series of support activities and, of course, other activities introduced to ensure feedback from students (Fig. 19).

Our particular concern with the creation of the Open University system lay in the use which could be made of educational technology to guide and facilitate the primary functional activity mentioned above.

It was therefore necessary to study the processes involved with a view to creating a satisfactory organizational structure to carry them out. The first step was to recognize, from the processes involved in the primary functional activity, likely boundaries for the sub-systems which would have to be set up. Boundaries are usually defined by discontinuities between processes— discontinuities in time, technology and space. A boundary implies a need for liaison and control between the sub-systems on either side. Further, a boundary which may be made a factor in deciding upon organizational structure needs to be considered not only in terms of the physical processes which it would separate but also in terms of the human groupings to which it would lead. Careful study of the primary functional activity model (Fig. 19), together with its implications for staffing, led us to identify four main sub-systems—the course team, a design sub-system, a television and radio technical sub-system and a 'business activities' sub-system. The last comprised production and marketing. Marketing was conceived as the operations required to package and store materials, and to distribute them to students, tutors and local study centres (since, in the Open University, the students will not come to the University, the University will go to the students, tutors and other staff all over the country using a variety of ways and means), and to sell University materials to institutional customers.

These functional sub-systems formed a basis for proposing alternative organizational structures which would be appropriate to carry out the primary functional activity processes.

A further crucial step is to indicate control mechanisms likely to be effective in regulating the overall system and in co-ordinating its sub-systemic parts. An important point in this connection is that if adaptation, feedback, evolution, self-regulation and so on, are to be achieved in practice, to however limited an extent, then the appropriate control mechanisms must arise from a sub-system superordinate to those sub-systems for which the mechanism has been devised. Such a superordinate system for control is often referred to as a 'meta-system'. Central to the idea of control are, of course, the nature,

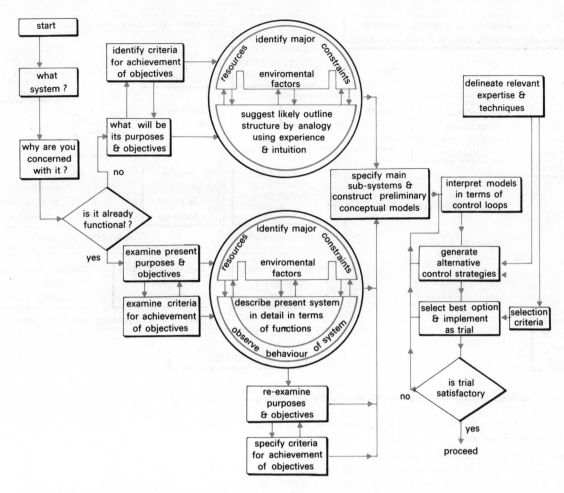

*Fig. 17  A 'systematic' approach to a problem, with only a hint of a 'systems' approach.
In practice, to convince those unfamiliar with systems ideas, it is best to use a systematic
approach first, with a minimum of technical jargon.*

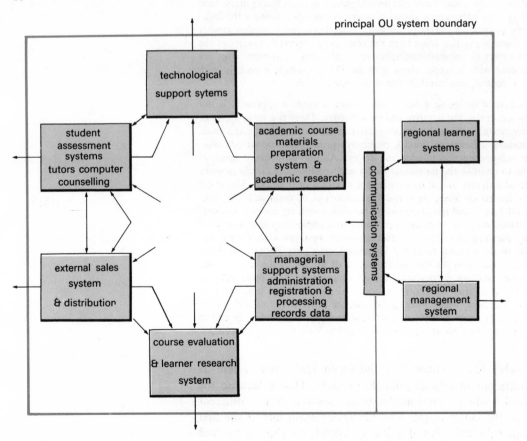

*Fig. 18   General interaction model. Open University major sub-systems.*

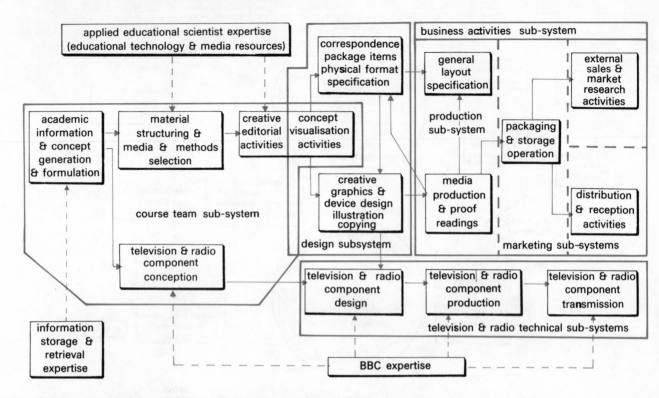

*Fig. 19   Course materials preparation, production and distribution. Preliminary functional model.*

timing and amounts of information flowing within the total system, and the way in which this information can be used.

Our terms of reference were mainly concerned with the roles of course teams and of the educational technology in supporting the course teams, and with the Vice-Chancellor's control and monitoring system. However, in attempting to adopt a total systems approach, especially with regard to control mechanisms, it was necessary to scan areas other than those representing the focal points of our terms of reference. In our present state of limited knowledge about the applications of general systems theory in practice, a total systems approach is always a severe compromise between the desirables, the acceptables and the practicables. A further severe limitation on what can be done in practice arises from the commonly observed inability of the systems expert to communicate effectively with decision makers who are not familiar with concepts about systems. Our approach, especially with regard to control, was therefore one of extreme caution.

The process of designing a new system, using a systems approach, is not linearly sequential, but iterative and evolutionary. There is a main sequence of operations through which one goes—activities defined by a systems approach. One outlines a functional model, recognizes primary functional activities, defines sub-systemic boundaries and so on. As one advances it becomes possible to improve the functional model and specify more clearly primary functional activities. Initial boundaries are modified or re-drawn. The whole process can be envisaged as a spiral arrangement of main activities with highly interactive and iterative linkages between points on the coil. In order to get started on a system design, there must be a preliminary specification of primary purposes and objectives. In the case of the Open University it was possible to derive these from the Planning Committees Report, the Vice-Chancellor and from the few members of staff in post at the time. At the same time, working parties were set up to provide much more detailed examinations of the University's educational concerns and practical procedures. Therefore, whilst working towards the achievement of preliminary objectives it becomes possible to continually refine and extend them and to assess how good we are at achieving them and to learn from our experience.

You will probably have noticed that the Open University system as described appears not to include you, the student. This is because the system as defined by the planners needed to be looked at from a different point of view in the initial stages. This illustrates again one of the first points I made that the definition of a system depends on who *you* are and what you are *trying to achieve*.

# Answers to examples

**Example 1**

If you read on you will see that two of my reasons are:

(1) the marbles or particles are not really linked or connected together so that they can affect each other,
(2) the 'system' does not behave—it does not do anything as a system because of the properties of the parts,

and a third is

(3) subtracting or adding a marble or particle makes no difference to the assembly.

**Example 2**

As you will see if you read on, the answer is 'many more than any of these'—many, many more in fact.

**Example 3**

The results for 1, 2, 3 and 4 components (each component being in one or other of two states) are listed in the table:

| number of two-state components | number of different system states |
|---|---|
| 1 | 2 or $2^1$ |
| 2 | 4 or $2^2$ |
| 3 | 8 or $2^3$ |
| 4 | 16 or $2^4$ |

So for $n$ two-state components there are $2^n$ possible different states for the whole system. You can probably see that with three possible states for each component, like a red, green or amber train signal, there will be $3^n$ possible states for the whole system (where $n =$ number of components as before).

**Example 4**

I calculated it like this:

I can choose any one of the four states A, B, C, or D to start with: the next state can only be one of three (remember A→A or C→C is not counted as a change), and the third state can again only be one of three since again I cannot follow an A with an A, etc. So I have $4 \times 3 \times 3$ possibilities $= 36$ for two changes. The next transition can likewise be to one of three states so for three successive changes I have $4 \times 3 \times 3 \times 3 = 108$ sequences.

The general rule for $n$ changes in this system (or two components, each being in one of their two states) is:

$$4 \times 3^n \text{ sequences.}$$

**Example 5**

This question is answered by J. E. Gordon in your set book *The new science of strong materials** on pp: 40 and 256. Read these pages and see if his explanation satisfies you. I must say I have a nagging doubt—why do the molecules curl up again when you take the pull off the rubber, are they all deformed?

**Example 6**

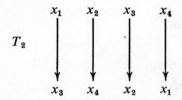

$T_2$

$x_1 \quad x_2 \quad x_3 \quad x_4$

$x_3 \quad x_4 \quad x_2 \quad x_1$

**Example 7**

$T_3$

| red light | flashing amber | green | amber |

| flashing amber | green | amber | red |

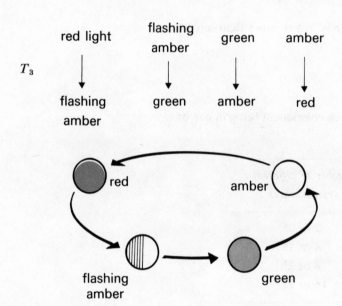

**Example 8**

$$T_4 \quad \begin{matrix} x = & 50 \\ y = & 4 \\ z = & 102 \end{matrix} \qquad T_4^2 \quad \begin{matrix} x = 25 \\ y = 8 \\ z = 54 \end{matrix} \qquad T_4^3 \quad \begin{matrix} x = 12.5 \\ y = 16 \\ z = 33 \end{matrix}$$

**Example 9**

operational research
ergonomics
ecology
cybernetics

* Gordon, J. E. (1968) *The new science of strong materials*, Penguin Books.

**Example 10**

The variety available in the system is the total number of different states it can take up. The three-light signal has three components and from our earlier examples this gives $2^3 = 8$ different states (remember that all lights *off* is one state). So the system could signal just 8 different messages but one of the signal states would be all lights off. This could not be distinguished from a power failure so it might be a rather dangerous state of the system to have to use. We could make it mean 'do not move past this signal under any circumstances' in which case it might be quite a useful signal to have available because it would *fail-safe*, i.e. a power failure would bring all traffic to a halt.

The present traffic lights give four messages:

| | |
|---|---|
| RED | STOP |
| GREEN | PROCEED WITH CAUTION |
| AMBER | STOP UNLESS YOU ARE PAST THE STOP LINE |
| RED AND AMBER | PREPARE TO GO |

So there are four unused states available and the system is only 50% used.

**Example 11**

There are a number of domestic examples you might have given. Cooking frequently involves open loop methods where the cook follows a set of instructions such as: 'cook for 20 minutes at 350°F then for one hour at 250°F'. Gardening also involves open loop control, possibly because the feedback of information takes so long! So fertilizer treatment, pruning by instruction and so on are open loop.

Other examples come from behaviour such as piano playing by sight reading where the fingers are put into position without looking at the keyboard, or going down a well-known flight of stairs without looking. Lastly, a doctor prescribing a course of treatment for a disease he recognizes is also exercising open loop control although in this case he will almost certainly check to see that the results are correct.

**Example 12**

This is not quite such a simple problem as it might at first appear. In an open loop system there is no connection between the output and input and the first question to answer is 'what are the input and output?' Remember that the engine has an input (steam or energy in hot steam) and an output (physical work done or energy expended) but this is not the control system, it is the engine.

The *control* system consists of the connection between the position of the beam (output) and the setting of the valves (input). When Humphrey Potter operated the engine, *he* provided the path which connected beam position to valve setting; when the mechanical links were put in *they* became the feedback route for the information about beam position to valve setting so the control system is a feedback system or a closed loop one.

**Appendix 1   Exercises on exponents**

| | | | |
|---|---|---|---|
| 1 | $2^4$ | 3 | $6^2$ |
| 2 | $5^3$ | 4 | $14^3$ |

5    $17^4$

6    $5^4 = 5 \times 5 \times 5 \times 5 = 625$

7    $10^4 = 10 \times 10 \times 10 \times 10 = 10\,000$

8    $17^4 = 17 \times 17 \times 17 \times 17 = 83\,521$

9    $2^6 = 2 \times 2 \times 2 \times 2 \times 2 \times 2 = 64$

10   $9^3 = 9 \times 9 \times 9 = 729$

11   $x^3 = x \times x \times x$

12   $y^4 = y \times y \times y \times y$

13   $22.4 \times 10^1$

14   $0.224 \times 10^2$

15   $22\,400$

16   $2240$

17   $2.24 \times 10^5$

18   $1.732 \times 10^4$

19   $169\,450\,000$

20   $1924$

21   $10^{-4}$

22   $\dfrac{1}{10^3}$

23   $\frac{1}{2} \times 10^{-3}$

24   $\dfrac{1}{200}$

25   $\dfrac{1}{14\,000}$

26   $\dfrac{1}{2400}$

27   $0.001\,73$

28   $0.006\,82$

29   $0.0749$

30   $16.832$

31   $0.000\,001\,01$

32   $7.06$

33   $\dfrac{1}{10.01} \times 10^{-2}$

34   $0.25 \times 10^{-4}$

# ACKNOWLEDGEMENTS

Grateful acknowledgement is made to the following sources for material used in this unit:

## TEXT

Chapman & Hall Ltd. for R. Ashby, *Design for a Brain*, 1960 and *Introduction to Cybernetics*, 1956; Harvard University Press for A. Angyal, *Foundations of a Science of Personality*, 1941; Institute of Management Sciences for K. Boulding, 'General systems theory: the skeleton of science' in *Management Science*, **2** (3) 1956; Kogan Page for M. W. Neil, A systems approach to course planning at the Open University', both in *The Systems Approach to Education and Training*, ed. A. J. Romiszowski, 1970; John Wiley & Sons Inc. for R. Ashby in *Views on General Systems Theory*, ed D. Mesarović, 1964; Professor Black of Bath University for the note on Harold S. Black (no relation); Professor P. B. Checkland of Lancaster University for his systems methodology.

## ILLUSTRATIONS AND TABLES

Blackwell Scientific Publications for Fig. 12 in *Journal of Animal Ecology*, **18,** 117, 1949; Commonwealth Scientific and Industrial Research Organisation for Fig. 11 in *Australian Journal of Zoology*, **2,** 9, 1954.

# T100 THE MAN-MADE WORLD
## Technology Foundation Course Units

| Week Number | Correspondence Text | Unit Number |
|---|---|---|
| 1, 2 | Modelling I | 4 |
| 3 | Design File | 32 |
| 4 | Systems | 1 |
| 5 | Control | 16 |
| 6 | Communication and Human Senses | 2 |
| 7 | Mechanics | 6 |
| 8, 9 | Electricity and Magnetism | 7/8 |
| 10, 11 | Energy Conversion/Power Society | 20/21 |
| 12 | Environment File | 23 |
| 13, 14 | Maintaining the Environment | 26/27 |
| 15 | Noise Abatement | S26/27 |
| 16 | Economics File | 11 |
| 17 | Structures and Microstructures | 9 |
| 18 | Materials | 22 |
| 19, 20 | Chemical Technology | 24/25 |
| 21 | Cities File | 30 |
| 22 | Automatic Computing | 12 |
| 23 | The Heart of Computers | 13 |
| 24 | Computer Systems | 14 |
| 25 | Economics of Traffic Congestion | 31 |
| 26 | Transport File | 31 File |
| 27, 28 | Design | 33/34 |
| 29 | Statistics and Reliability | 10 |
| 30 | Modelling II | 18 |
| 31 | Production Systems Modelling | 28 |
| 32 | The Production Environment | 29 |